I am

Work by the children of
Scoil Íosagáin and
St. Mura's National School,
Buncrana, County Donegal.

First published in 1999 by
Scoíl Íosagáin,
St. Mary's Road, Buncrana,
County Donegal, Ireland.

Design and Print Management by
Scríptoríum,
Carrowkeel, Castlebaldwin,
County Sligo, Ireland.

A CIP CATALOGUE RECORD FOR THIS BOOK
IS AVAILABLE FROM THE BRITISH LIBRARY
ISBN 0 9536144 0 9

With gratitude to the Board of Managers of
Scoil Íosagáin, Buncrana
and to the artists:

Visual Artists: Aileen Barr
                    Marie Barrett
                    Bairbre Geraghty
                    Marie Houston

Creative Writers: Joan Newmann
                    Kate Newmann

Dramatist: Patricia Doherty

Musicians: Eleanor Lamb
                    Lorna McLaughlin

Dancers: Ciara Bradley
                    Ayesha Mailey

Story-tellers: Sheila Quigley
                    Billy Teare
                    Liz Weir

for Shaun, Oran and James
and
Fernando and Rocío

At 3.10pm on the 15th August 1998 a bomb exploded in Omagh killing 31 men women and children and injuring hundreds of others. Among the dead was Shaun McLaughlin (12) and Oran Doherty (8), pupils from Scoil Íosagáin, Buncrana. Shaun and Oran, along with other boys and girls from Buncrana had travelled to Omagh with a group of Spanish Students to visit the Ulster American Folk Park and later to go shopping. The Spanish Students had been attending a Summer Language School based at Scoil Íosagáin. Integration with the local children was actively encouraged hence the inclusion of the boys and girls from Buncrana on the trip. Fernando Blasco Baselga (12) and Rocio Abad Ramos (23), both from Madrid, also lost their lives in the explosion along with James Barker (12) who had moved with his family from England to live in Buncrana only a year earlier.

Other pupils and past pupils from Scoil Íosagáin witnessed the terrible incident and were among the injured. The whole school community was devastated by the deaths of Shaun and Oran. Parents, teachers and children are struggling to come to terms with the death of a son, a brother, a friend, a cousin, a pupil, a classmate, a neighbour. The loss of innocent life in such a cruel random manner is sometimes difficult to accept and almost impossible to comprehend. And yet as we try to deal with our feelings of disbelief, anger, pain and frustration we know we have embarked on a journey, a long, frightening and sometimes lonely journey of grief, which we hope in time will help us to cope with our loss and eventually lead us to recovery. To guide us on our journey we have used an Arts Education Programme in an attempt to help our pupils express their feelings and thoughts through the medium of art, drama, music, dance and creative writing. The aim of the Programme is to explore and celebrate the differences in our community leading to an understanding and acceptance of difference in religion, culture, age and ability. By offering the pupils new experiences and inviting them to look closely at who they are and where their place is, they have learned a language which has enabled them to express their feelings about life, death, family, friendship, togetherness, separation, war and peace. This book is a celebration of that expression. It is a precious collection of personal hopes and fears, observation and understanding, as recounted by 150 5th and 6th class pupils, who speak honestly about themselves and their world. It is dedicated to the memory of Shaun and Oran, James, Fernando and Rocio and all who died in Omagh on August 15th 1998.

I would like to thank all who have been involved in this beautiful creation. To the 5th and 6th class pupils of Scoil Íosagáin and to St. Mura's National School for their honesty and enthusiasm in their writing; to their teachers Miriam Burns, Josephine Doherty, Elizabeth Gill, Christine Johnston, Brid McGrenaghan and Rosemary Dunne for their encouragement and patience. And especially to Joan Newmann and Kate Newmann for their inspiration. It has been a privilege for all of us to work with Joan and Kate. They have gently moved us along on our journey of grief. They have given us the words to help us, not only to speak but to listen, not only to question but to reflect, not only to laugh but to cry.

Give sorrow words; the grief, that does not speak,
Whispers the o'er-fraught heart, and bids it break.

> Macbeth
> act iv, scene iii.

Sinead McLaughlin

8

Liam Grant

I AM
I am the day the bomb ripped out the heart of Omagh.
I am the second before my friend died, before a bit of me died.
I am the computer world that is open to me.
I am the shortness of life.
I am the small earth but the immense space.

MY FIRST MEMORY
It was a hole in the living room for the T.V. I can remember the man using a drill and he looks at me staring. I have to be told I was only two years old at the time.

MY PLACE IS
My place is the old sixties wallpaper.
My place is the old floorboard that makes it hard to escape.
My place is the printer that moves the whole house when I print my homework.
My place is the door that will not open.
My place is the red chair from an old warship.

THE BEST PERSON
My friend is (I know her as 011). I can tell her anything I could never, I would not, tell my mum or dad. I knew her for two years. She lived in a cancer ward in some hospital and died a few months ago. I keep her E-mail as if they were the keys to my heart.

MY WORST DAY
My worst day was when I woke up on Sunday morning to find that Shaun had died in the Omagh bomb. I thought it was cold and dark but bright. The place I was told he had died is gone now, like Shaun - at peace.

CURRANT
It is a currant.
It is a Christmas smell.
In the light it can be black or brown.
It is fermented Guinness left on the bar for the night.
It is the hand of old people.

Patricia Grant

I AM
I am the first time I got a dancing dress.
I am the first time I went to a wedding. I got lots of money.

I am the first time I spoke my Spanish.
I am the first time I went to a Feis and won medals.
I am.the first time I went to the swimming pool. I was scared.

DREAM

I was lying sleeping in my bed. I dreamt that I was clerking on my own
and a big bright light came over the altar and I looked up and it was Shaun
- he had come to help me clerk. I woke up crying and I ran into my
mummy's and daddy's bed.

I had another dream that I was in the Omagh bomb and I see my mother
lying there without her legs. I woke up and I see my mother up in the
kitchen and she said nothing like that would happen again.

FIRE

Fire can destroy a lot of things.
It can make a small thing into a big thing.
Daddy puts a fire in the fireplace and that gives us heat.
When a house goes on fire people can die and get seriously injured.
The Apostles saw a tongue of red and it is the sign of fire.

MY FIRST MEMORY

On my third birthday I climbed up on a chair to put on the Christmas tree
lights and I fell down and split my chin and had to get fifteen stitches.
When I was four I fell over a wall and fell into a big deep barrel.

EGG

It is the sun in the middle of water.
It feels slimy.
It tastes like hard bread.
It sounds like little pebbles shaking inside a shell.
It smells like burned bacon.

MY BEST DAY, MY WORST DAY

My worst day was when I heard the bomb had gone off in Omagh.
My best day was when my dog had four pups.

Gerard Doherty

SHAUN

Walking down the town
Guided into the bomb he's

10

Happy in Heaven

MY PLACE IS
My place is the garage that me and my two friends practise in.
My place is the smell of furniture polish when you come in.
My place is the sound feedback because of the small size.
My place is the atmosphere when you walk in.
My place is the way it is cold at first but it naturally gets warmer.
My other place is Buncrana because of the friendly people.

TEN WORDS FOR A DESERT ISLAND
HELLO; DAD; MUM; WHERE? WHEN? HOW? WHY?
YES; SWEETS; FRIENDS.

ONE WORD FOR A DESERT ISLAND
WHY?

MY FIRST MEMORY
My first memory is when I was four years old. I had a toy turtle (you had
to pull it along). And then one day I fell on top of it and smashed it; and I
had a blue pair of dungarees and always wore them. I remember my pram
and buggy. Me and my sister sat in it. And my first bo-bo of tea.

BLACK
Black tastes like berries.
Black feels like coal.
Black looks like stars in the sky at night time.
Black smells like chalk on the board.
Black reminds me of Metallica.
Black sounds like bats screeching.

WATER
It looks like water in the pool.
It tastes like snow on top of cars.
It smells like disinfectant spread all over the toilet.
It feels like water from the tap.
It sounds like a leak from the pipe.
I saw it on the ground, dogs cooling down in it.
I heard it out my back yard when my dog was drinking.

RED
Tastes like a sweet glass of red wine.

It is the big red stain on a white shirt.
It is the smelly cork of a bottle left in a cupboard for years.
It is the deep splashing into a thin glass.
It feels like an unripe gooseberry.

TURF
It reminds me of our garage filled with turf and mice.
It looks like a city in ruins after an earthquake.
It sounds like the heavy hooves of a horse galloping across Swan Park.
It feels like a cracked stone.

MY WORST DAY, MY BEST DAY
My worst day was when I heard Shaun and Oran were dead. My knees
weakened and I fell down some stairs. It was the day I thought my sister
was dead as well of the bomb.

The best day was when my uncle came over from Canada for Christmas
about four years ago, with a lot of different Canadian foods. I only saw
him once in my life but I remember him clearly.

BRIDGE HAIKU
I'm about to cross
When it collapses on me
And I am falling.

Elizabeth Curran
DREAM
I am standing in the middle of a crowded room. I am quiet and bored. I
am talking to the dog who looks like he is hypnotised. I haven't got a
thing to do except stare at the flurry of activity around me. I don't know
what's going on at all. Lots of people are talking and there is a lot of food
on the table which no-one is eating.

MY PLACE IS
My place is the ticking clock on the wall in the kitchen.
My place is the yellow on my wall in my bedroom.
My place is the warm welcoming fire in the sitting-room.
My place is the warmth of my bedroom when I walk in.
My place is the way the hall smells like incense that my mum burns on
top of the piano.
My place is the way my home makes me feel safe and secure.

YELLOW
Is the sunshine shining through my bedroom window.
It is bananas being sliced at the cutting board.
It is the wall in my bedroom that I hang my posters on.
It is the big bright sign that says SALE in the shop window.
It would smell like custard.

LEMON
It tastes sour and brings tears to my eyes.
It has a tingly feeling that makes you want to squeal.
Its skin looks sunny and bright like a torchlight in the dark.

RAISIN
It looks like the pupil of an eye.
It is soft like my granny's wrinkles.
When I drop it on the table it sounds like the little noise people make
when they're creeping around in the middle of the night.
It tastes like a hard piece of chewing gum.

Rita-Marie Doherty

I AM
I am the excited day of my sister's wedding.
I am the time, 3.10 on the 15th of August.
I am the nervous day of my Communion.
I am the nervous day I start the Convent.
I am the glad day I got my hair cut.
I am the happy day when summer begins.
I am the very very happy day our teacher will never do work.

MY FIRST MEMORY
It is my fifth birthday. All of my nieces and friends came. I remember my
blue dress. It was silk and beautiful. I still have it and it gathers dust so some
time I might give it to one of my nieces. I always remember my fifth birthday party. I can still smell the perfume off it.

MY BEST DAY, MY WORST DAY
My worst day was the 15th of August, 1998. I was in the Omagh bomb.
It was very scary while we had to lie on grass for three-and-a-half hours.
It was terrible. I will always remember that tragic day. All I could see and
smell that day was smoke.

My best day was in Omagh as well when I went to meet Boyzone. We met the new band too. Their name was West Side. It was brilliant. I will always remember my best day.

PURPLE

It looks like the Turkish skirt I was going to get for my Confirmation.
It tastes like grapes.
It sounds like the purple marker scraping off a page so quick.
It feels like the Turkish trousers in Dunnes Stores.
It smells like the ink of a purple marker on the page.

LEMON

It smells like an orange.
It looks like a quarter of the sun.
It tastes like the piece of fruit you get in a jug of water.
It feels like a raw cut just ready to be plastered.
It sounds like a rubber banging off the table.

DREAM

My dream was about my sister Zoe dying and she came back to me and said she was coming back. A few days later I found out she was expecting a baby. I always think now, if I dream about someone dying, that at least someone I know is going to have a baby. It didn't really make sense because a dead person doesn't come back. It was like a nightmare, but when she came to my house a few days after, it was brilliant news. I hope I dream that about another sister because I'd like another niece or nephew.

BRIDGE HAIKU

Some bridges are high
And some others are so low
Bridges part things too

EARTH

It reminds me of the clay going down on the coffin of my grannies.
It reminds me of my daddy going out the back to get worms for fishing.
Earth is our life.
Earth has beautiful things in it.

Leanne Porter

I AM

I am the day I cried when my daddy went to work in America.
I am the day I would not go up the aisle to be my uncle's flower-girl.
I am the day I started school.

I am the day I made my Holy Communion.
I am the day my little yellow budgie died.
I am the day I learnt to cycle my bike.
I am the day I went on my first holiday.

RED
It sounds like men shouting, getting into a fire-engine.
It feels like soft velvet cloth.
It tastes like tomato ketchup all over chips.
It looks like the red light flashing on the sea.
It smells like the roses in summer in my granny's garden.

DREAM
These people were after me and there was no way of getting away from
them. All these people I knew kept coming into it and I had no idea where
they were coming out of. It was so scary. I woke up in a sweat and I
couldn't get back to sleep.

THE BEST PERSON
The best person is my little brother Colm. He is so important to me. I used to
be the youngest, but not any more. He's always there smiling, waiting for me
home from school. When my friends are in my house he never leaves us alone
to do our own thing. He has his own bedroom but he keeps sleeping in mine.

EARTH
Earth smells like the garden in summer.
Earth feels like my dog when he has rolled in the garden.
Earth looks like the dirty footprints on the floor after the dog's been in.

TURF
It sounds like someone throwing turf into the fire out of the bucket.

Maria Fullerton

I AM
I am the Sunday dinner my granny makes.
I am the story my mammy used to read to me.
I am the games my dad used to play with me.
I am the day I made my first Holy Communion.
I am the day I was flower-girl for my uncle.

MY BEST DAY

The best day of my life was when my sister was born. I already had a brother and I was looking forward to having a sister to play with. She was very small and I got to hold her any time I wanted to. I also got to share my bedroom with her.

BLUE

Looks like the sky on a bright summer day.
Feels like a big silk blanket.
Smells like fish that have just been caught.
Sounds like the birds singing.
Tastes like a cold drink of water.

Bobby McColgan

I AM

I am the time that my cousin was born.
I am the time that I had to see him.
I am the time that he came home.
I am the time of his first birthday.
I am the time he fell and hurt his head.

MY FIRST MEMORY

I remember the time my mummy was making buns and when she was making chocolate and she dropped some on the fire and I went over and touched it and I burned my belly and got a scar.

MY BEST DAY, MY WORST DAY

One of my best days was when my cousin was born.
One of my worst days is when Shaun died.

DREAM

I had a dream about long ago. It was about when I was on holiday and I was in the water with my surf-board, and when it hit me on the back it was very sore and the next day I woke up and I had to go to the doctor.

THE BEST PERSON

My best person is my granny because she always gives me money when I stay and when we go to Derry she always gets me something nice.

BRIDGE HAIKU

HOW CAN WE KNOW WHAT
IS WAITING ON THE OTHER

Gareth Bradley

I AM
I am the apple-tart my granny makes me.
I am the money my mammy gives me.
I am the friends that I have.
I am the day my granda died.
I am the day I met Shaun.

MY FIRST MEMORY
I remember when my sister and I got our photo taken in my granny's house, and her dog jumped up on me and left me all dirty.

BLACK
Smells like oil.
Tastes like liquorice.
Looks like an empty room without a light.
Feels like soot when you're cleaning out the fireplace.
Sounds like Rose, the school secretary, speaking through the speakers.

MY PLACE IS
My bedroom, the way the wind makes a whistle blowing through my skylight window.

MY BEST DAY, MY WORST DAY
One of my worst days was when my granda died.
One of my best days was when my little sister was born.

EGG
Reminds me of a full moon.

DREAM
One night I had a nightmare. I was getting chased by a kidnapper. My mammy and daddy were right beside me but they would not do anything. I couldn't run fast, it was like I was in slow motion. The kidnapper nearly caught me, but just then my mammy woke me up and said *Hurry up and get ready for school - it's half past eight.*

Edward McCallion

I AM

I am the time I was given the jumper that I didn't like.
I am the day that my Gran gave me the money to buy whatever I liked.
I am the time I had to stand outside in the cold to wait for the milkman to tell him a message.
I am the day I fell down the stairs and hurt my ankle.

BLUE

Tastes like a blue lollypop.
Feels like a puddle of water.
Sounds like a whale splashing into the water.
Looks like a clear sky.

WATER

Tastes like flat lemonade.
Looks like a clear bottle of medicine.
Sounds like water from a slow stream.

SILVER

Smells like a delicious meal cooking in my Mum's silver saucepan.
Looks like a dark cloud in the sky.
Sounds like an orchestra in a theatre.
Reminds me of my neighbour's new car.

EGG

An egg reminds me of a lovely yellow moon in a dark black sky.
An egg smells like a stone from the beach.
An egg feels like a runny nose.

GOLD

Gold looks like a crown on a King, with sparkling diamonds.
Gold tastes like a meal cooking in a fancy posh hotel.
Gold sounds like people betting in a casino.
Gold reminds me of a golden coat of fur on a lion.

EARTH

Earth can be riddled up into small pieces.
Earth smells like a piece of food trapped for a long time.

Ronan Bradley

MY FIRST MEMORY

Going up the town to see Santa with the Fire Brigade.

SALT
It reminds me of chips.
It is little white dots.
It feels like watered ice.
It sounds like cracking.
It tastes like the pool.
It feels like a blue car door.
It sounds like ocean waves and a boat against a rock.

I AM
I am the Sunday dinner.
I am the page-boy suit I have to wear.
I am the candle I lit in Chapel.

MY PLACE IS
My place is the way I dive in the water at the beach.
My place is the snow gliding from the sky.
My place is the walk around Swan Park.
My place is the fishing season at the Crana River.

RICE
It looks like worms just born.
They stick in your teeth.
Mostly they are seen in a Chinese restaurant.
They also look like maggots in a box.
It tastes like gum.
It smells like the tip of my pencil.

POSTCARD
I was standing there selling blankets and there was a smell of fish. That's why not too many people came and bought, but a woman bought my best sheet. It had a lovely smell of freshness. Across from me a man was selling apples very fast. That's where most of the people went. In all that day I sold six sheets and made one pounds fifty, and got three sheets stolen.

LEMON
It has a smell of an orange split ice-cream.
It is a gum shield of a boxer.
It makes you shiver if you bite it.

THE BEST PERSON
The best person is the man who sells cheap games for the Play Station.

He sells games that are forty-five pounds for nine pounds. He lives about a hundred metres away from me and I know him well. Sometimes he gives me a game for five pounds.

CONFIRMATION HAIKU

A new name taken
For that important day, my
Godparents will help.

WHITE

It is the furry back of a running rabbit.
It is the clouds floating across the sky.
It is a white shirt if you use the right detergent.

EARTH

It reminds me of American Spice Beef.
It looks like the stuff you put in a grave.

Adrian Cutliffe

GOLD

Gold feels like a millionaire.
Gold smells of coins.
Gold tastes like butter.
Gold looks like taps on a bath.

MY BEST DAY

My best day was yesterday when I won a TV in a competition in a paper.
I feel very happy and joyful.

EGG

It reminds me of the sun going down.
It smells of the sea.
It sounds like a frog jumping into the water.

RED

It sounds like the Fire Brigade
It feels like danger up ahead
It tastes like an apple
It smells like blood
It looks like a teacher getting very mad

AIR

Air is very light

Your breath is air
You go to the airport
A balloon is air
Air can reach speeds of a hundred miles per hour

Finian McNutt

BRIDGE

The water is calm
Flowing past under the bridge
It goes quite quickly

FIRE

It is welcoming.
It's hot and it burns you.
It warms your house.
It kills a lot of people.
Fire reminds me of the devil and his evil ways.

AIR

If there is no air we would die.
Air is a cool breeze on a hot day.
Air is life.
Air reminds me of a bird flying.

YELLOW

Yellow is the sand at the beach.
It is the smell of melted butter.
Yellow tastes like hot custard ready to eat.
Yellow is the moon on a warm night.
Yellow feels smooth and soft.

MY BEST DAY

My best day was when my Mum and Dad told me I was going on holiday. I was
very excited. I went to Scotland. I had a good time and I would like to go back.

LENT

I haven't made up my mind what I'm going off for Lent. I think hard
about it, but I don't think I'll be able to stay off them all Lent.

MY PLACE IS

My place is the football club.
My place is the boys cheering when you score.

My place is the way when you lose, you're in a bad mood.
My place is the referee who sends you off.

MY FIRST MEMORY
My first memory is when I was four, I knocked over the TV but it didn't break. I tried to pick it up and I couldn't. I called my brother and told him to help me and we got it up.

Maria Doherty

GREEN
Looks like the fresh green grass in the meadow.
Tastes like green beans with your Sunday dinner.
Green sounds like an evergreen tree when it's surrounded by snow.
Green smells like the liqiud you put around your toilet rim.
Green feels like a lawn-mower cutting the grass on a hot summer day.

TURF
It looks like a piece of turf burning on the open fire.
It smells like something rotting outside waiting to be thrown away.
It feels like a rough ball rubbing against smooth skin.
It sounds like a star dropping out of the night sky.

MY BEST DAY
My best day was when I saw my little cousin being born in hospital. And my first day at school when I met two of my best friends, Sarah and Rita-Marie. I remember the smell of my granny's perfume leaving me at the school gate. I remember the sound of the classroom door shutting on the first day at school.

SALT
It feels like grains of sand running through my hand.
It tastes like some rotting water to be swallowed.
It sounds like hundreds and thousands getting sprinkled on a hot cake.

DREAM
A dream I had was when I met my granda for the first time. The year was 1977. He took me on a bus to go and visit the zoo in Belfast and then he disappeared. I looked around for him, but I couldn't find him. When I woke up it seemed very real, but I realised it was only a dream.

FIRE
Fire is a hot flame burning.

It is the fire burning the rainforest.
It is a flame of silence.
Fire gives you warmth and comfort.
Fire is the welcoming glow.

I AM
I am the day when I met my five best friends.
I am the day when I helped my granny bake bread.
I am the day I was my cousin's flower-girl.
I am the day when the school week ends.
I am the day my cousin was born.

MY FIRST MEMORY
Was when I was sitting on Santa's knee in Derry.

Alan Fletcher
I AM
I am the friend that supports me through hard times and bad.
I am the parent that keeps the roof over my head.
I am the teacher that gives me a piece of her mind.
I am the ball, and which net it's in, even if we always win.

MY FIRST MEMORY
My first memory is playing football with Patrick Fletcher in the park.

RED
Red tastes like lip-stick.
Red looks like a sunset.
Red feels smooth like vanilla ice-cream.
Red sounds like someone calling for help.
Red smells like a rose in summer time.

WATER
Smells fresh like salmon.
Feels like a soft stream.
Looks like an ocean and its waves.
Sounds like spet splat of a fish.
Tastes like the last drop of water when you're sick.

GREEN
Green is the peas in the pot.
It is the grass blowing like your hair.

It is the forty shades of green in Ireland.
It is the football players sprinting up the wing.
It sounds like the colour so quiet I fall asleep.

MY PLACE IS
The beach and its sand wrinkles.
The dog that ripped my trousers.
The book where I drift away into another world.
The town where I meet my friends.

TURF
It feels hard to crush.
It smells of a burned-out fire.
It sounds like it's screaming when the man kills it with the spade.
It looks like a bit of pork chop.
It tastes like cigarettes and the smoke.

RAISIN
It feels like an elastic band.
It smells like a Christmas cake.
It tastes like a black pudding.
It sounds like a black pebble hitting off a car.
It looks like a full stop.

POSTCARD
I am the dog, curious and clever.
I am looking at the people in poverty.
I am looking at one man, his fishing rod, trying to catch some fish.
The women are talking.
I have been looking for something to eat.
I am very weak and I cannot walk and I'm soon to die if I don't get something to eat.
I am sitting, bark barking for something to eat.

THE BEST PERSON
My best person is my teacher. She helps me through hard times and bad. She sticks up for me when I started my new class and I was being bullied. She talks to me and I talk to her. She teaches me maths, history, geography, English. I hate school and teachers, but I know that they will give me a life to live to get a job and a wife.

Stephen Doherty

EGG
It reminds me of getting a ducking on my birthday.
It sounds like when you crack it off the pan.
It reminds me of all those chocolate Easter eggs I get.
The yolk looks like the sun in the sky with no clouds.

BLUE
Blue tastes like when your pen is burst and you don't know.
Blue sounds like when you're scribbling on a page with a blue pen.
Blue looks like when you're in the middle of the sea and all you can see is the deep blue sea.

LEMON
It looks like a strip from the rainbow.

RAISIN
It looks like a dead beetle.

RICE
They look like very small maggots.
It sounds like hailstones hitting off the skylight window in my room.
It smells like sweaty hands, because when you pick them up they are that small you can't smell them.

MY WORST DAY
The worst day for me was when I heard that there was a bomb in Omagh and my friend Shaun and my cousin Oran had been killed in it.

UNDER THE BRIDGE
The way the rocks are shaped like chairs for you to sit on.
The way the river floods it when it is raining heavily.
The way no-one can get in but me.
The way it smells after a flood.

TURF
It is the sight of the old barn full of turf behind my house.
It reminds me of a scar when you pick it and it isn't on for long enough.
It reminds me of the bag men collecting it.

MY FIRST MEMORY
When I was about two years of age I used to sleep beside my mummy in a cot. If my mother let go of my finger in the middle of the night I would start crying.

I used to be afraid of the rain.

SALT

It smells like the sea.
It sounds like a lorry dumping sand.

Brendan Halpin

WATER

It smells like water from the sea.
It looks like a mirror.
It tastes like an ice-cube.
It sounds like a bashing against the rocks.

CREAM

Smells like a cold ice-cream on a hot day.
Looks like the Charlton away top.
Tastes like an ice-pop.
Sounds like cream falling off a cake.
Feels like butter on your toast.

MY PLACE IS

The only place I can get peace in the house.

MY WORST DAY

The worst day of my life was when I heard that Shaun was dead. I didn't really think it happened, because you don't think anybody you know would ever die. I was very sad and annoyed about what happened to Shaun and I will never forget him.

CONFIRMATION HAIKU

YOU PICK A SAINT'S NAME
MY GODPARENT WILL BE THERE
JUST LIKE BAPTISM.

THE BEST PERSON

My Dad is my best person because he takes me to a Celtic match every year. When we're not at a match he takes me in to watch it. He always gives me money and he helps me with my homework. He never gets mad with me either.

AIR

It keeps us alive.

And it's not up in space.
It also destroys with its fierce force.
It's what keeps a kite up in the sky.
It keeps you cool on a hot day.

EARTH

You plant seeds in it
And they grow to be flowers
And it is a home for worms.
It is really wet and soggy
When it is raining
And it feels like when I take the mud
Off my football boots.

Pio Grant

I AM

I am the family who love me.
I am the Play Station which I always play.
I am the TV which is very valuable to me.
I am the day my birthday comes.
I am the PC which we play during the day.
I am the days my granny comes to visit.

MY FIRST MEMORIES

My fifth birthday when some of my friends came up. We were playing musical
chairs and the chair broke with my friend sitting on it.
My first day in the pool when I jumped in and my two arm-bands burst.

MY WORST DAY

Is when my grandad died. There was a phone-call. I was in the kitchen.
My dad came in crying and at about five the priest came and took my dad
to my grandad's house. They came back later and took me and my mum up.

EGG

It smells like sour milk.
It looks like chip pan oil.
It feels like melting oil running through hands.
It sounds like inside a hen house.
It tastes like a chocolate Easter egg.

DREAM
I have a dream that I could drive at my age and own my own two-seater yellow convertible Porsche. And I would drive to school every day and be a rally driver.

BRIDGE HAIKU
Bridge helps us to cross
A river and to get from
One to another.

FIRE
Fire is a welcoming home in a cold house.
It is very dangerous because I know some people that were playing and set the field on fire and the Fire Brigade came to put it out.

Edward Cuffe

RED
Red looks like blood coming out of a busted nose.

I AM
I am the day we got no homework.
I am the day Liverpool win the League again.
I am the day Man United get relegated.

MY FIRST MEMORY
I was cycling my bike for a good while and I fell off and split my head. I had to get four stitches.

I was playing outside with my brother. I was chasing him. He ran in and I ran after him. He closed the door and I tried to stop it with my hand. My hand went through the glass and split my wrist.

GREEN
Green looks like apples falling from a tree.
Green smells like the inside of an apple-pie.
Green feels like the round nest of an apple.
Green sounds like the breeze going through the grass.

MY PLACE IS
My place smells of hot-dogs and chips walking outside when the night is over.
My place looks like a muddy road after the night.
My place sounds like the roar of a crowd when they score a goal.
My place feels like the players scoring.

MY WORST DAY

My worst day was when I heard about the Omagh bomb.
I thought that nobody died on that day. The next day, Sunday, I was really
upset when I woke up. Because when I woke up I heard that my best friend
had died and his name was Shaun, and the other twenty-eight people had
died and hundreds of people injured.

EGG

One time when my mummy was making a fry I got an egg. I cracked it open
and there was blood inside the egg.

BLACK

Black tastes like liquorice.
Black smells like a piece of burning coal.
Black sounds like coal coming out of a bag and into a bucket.
Black looks like coke in a glass.
Black feels like a black fluffy jumper.

AIR

Air is your oxygen.
Air is your life.
Air is warm days.
Air is cold nights.

Sarah McDaid

MY PLACE

Is the smell like oranges.
The sound of my place is my dogs barking outside.
My place is purple and yellow.
My place is bouncy because I bounce on my bed.
My place would taste like oranges.

MY WORST DAY

The worst day for me was when my brother Shane moved to America last
year on 11th August. We left him to the bus depot in Derry. It was very sad
because it was the first time anyone in my family moved away from home.
I can still hear the engine of the bus driving away.

POSTCARD

I am carrying this woman on my back and I am getting really hot and tired.
I still have to go a long way and this woman weighs a ton. She keeps on

whipping me with her whip to tell me to go faster. She is sitting to one end
of me so it is heavy on one side and not on the other. I can't wait to get home
to have a rest and a drink.

BLUE
Blue looks like a blue sky on a hot summer's day.
Blue smells like oil spilt on the road.
Blue tastes like ink when your pen bursts and it's all over your mouth.
Blue feels like the chlorine against you when you swim in the pool.

RAISIN
It tastes like grapes.
It sounds like someone digging a grave.

DREAM
I had a dream one time. All my friends were in it and we were stranded on
a desert island. We had nowhere to sleep at night or to eat. I don't know
how we got on the island, but then a small boat came along with nobody
in it. We got a mile out to sea but the boat started to sink. I started to
scream and I woke up screaming.

FIRE
Fire looks like the sun setting far away.
It sounds like the fire in your sitting-room cackling.
Fire does not have a feeling.
I have never tasted fire.

Majella McGlinchey

TIME HAIKU
Time is slow and fast
The time in school goes so slow
I wish it went fast

I AM
I am the day I went to a Boyzone concert. My friend was on a crutch.
I am the day I started school when I cried for my mummy.
I am the day I made my First Communion. I had a party.
I am the friend I have in Spain.
I am the friends I have.

BLACK
Black tastes like a liquorice bon-bon.

Black smells like burnt toast.
Black feels like velvet.
Black sounds like people shouting.
Black looks like a witch's hat or a cauldron.

RED

Red tastes like the blood in my mouth after a visit to the dentist.
Red sounds like a girl screaming after falling and cutting herself.
Red looks like fresh strawberries in summer.
Red feels like the berries on the holly tree.
Red smells like cherry sweets.

MY WORST DAY

My worst day was the 15th August when the bomb went off in Omagh injuring my Spanish friends and killing three boys from Buncrana. Everyone was silent. We all felt angry and sad.

POSTCARD

I am crocheting. I feel very bored because I hate crocheting and I can't see through my glasses properly. I smell sea water because the beach is quite near. It's a windy day so I can hear waves. I can still taste the tea I drank an hour ago because it was so strong.

DREAM

I remember a strange dream. I was on my own and no-one was about and I was trying to swim home. I was wakened by the call of my mammy waking me for school.

AIR

Air is every breath that you take.
Air is life.
Air is a balloon at a party.
Air is invisible.
Air is calm.

Kelly Lavelle

MY PLACE IS

My place is the attic that only I go up to.
My place is the front garden in which I sit with my dog.
My place is the computer room where I go after my homework is done.
My place is the bedroom which is only mine and I can sit alone in it and think.

My place is the sitting-room where I do my homework and watch television.

TURF
It looks like earth dug up.
It feels rough and hard like a stone.
It smells like fresh soil.
It sounds like someone knocking on the door.
It tastes like a hardened piece of soil my dog dug up from the flower bed.

WATER
It looks clear as a glass.
It sounds like a dripping sound.
It tastes very cool.
It feels smooth and wet but if you touch it it stays on your fingers.

GREEN
Green looks like the hills above where I live.
Green tastes like cabbage freshly cooked.
Green smells like Ireland with all the mountains.
Green sounds like all the instruments playing in the St. Patrick's Day Parade.

POSTCARD
I am cooking sausages. The sausages are on sticks and are going straight onto the fire. I feel hot from the fire on my face and I can't wait till the sausages are finally cooked. I would rather be at home in the house, but I have to make dinner. It is a cold day, so I am half warm and half cold. The front of me is hot from the fire and behind me I am cold from the cold air.

DREAM
When I was really young I used to have a nightmare that there were snakes in my bed. I didn't like them and thought I saw them everywhere. My parents used to have to come into my bedroom and show me that there were no snakes. When we had to go to school the next morning, everybody was mad at me for keeping them all awake last night. I kept on having nightmares about them night after night. Soon they got used to it, but were still very annoyed that every night I woke them all up thinking snakes were in my bed.

MY FIRST MEMORY
My memory was when I was five years old and visited Santa and didn't know who it was so I started crying.

Grainne Coleman

BROWN
It smells like fresh toast in the morning.
It tastes like toffee sweets.
It looks like wet sand on the beach.
It sounds like a man cutting down a tree.
It smells like brown sauce going through your fingers.

MY PLACE IS
The smell of fresh washed clothes.
My place is the sound of birds chirping.
My place is the feel of blankets.
My place is the taste of the fresh air coming through the window.

MY BEST DAY, MY WORST DAY
My best day was when my brother was born. I went to the hospital to see him.
My worst day was when my uncle died.

TURF
It smells like the fresh turf my granda takes home.
It feels like a hard rock hitting off your head.
It sounds like pebbles crashing together on the beach.
It looks like a small boat sailing across the sea.

LENT
During Lent I go off sweets and chocolate.
When it comes to Easter we are allowed to eat them again.
My uncle says that you're allowed to eat sweets every Sunday during Lent.

EGG
Looks like a sunflower.

POSTCARD
It feels very hot. It looks like the bulls running along the path. It looks like the logs across the bulls' back. It feels very bumpy. It sounds like the grunts from the bulls. It sounds like the bulls' hooves across the path.

RED
Looks like the red hair dye my sister put on her hair.
Red smells like a hot summer's day.
Red sounds like a robin red breast singing in a tree.
Red tastes like tomato soup.

Red feels like the red hot sun hitting off the back of my neck.

DREAM
When I was young my sister used to tell me that the bogey man was going to get me. I used to have nightmares that he was going to get me when I was sleeping and take me away.

THE BEST PERSON
My best person is my granny Ellen. I used to go over to her farm to see her. She used to let me walk around the farm. She let me and my sister name two of her cats. She was very kind and friendly. I miss her now because she died a few years ago.

Bernadette Gaynor

MY FIRST MEMORY
I fell off my bike and I went over the handlebars and my middle fingernail was coming off.

I AM
I am the time when my baby sister was born.
I am the time I go to see my granny in Dublin.
I am the time I went to meet Michelle Smith.
I am when I made my Communion.
I am the time when I moved from Dublin and started my new school.

TURF
It feels hard and jaggy.
It smells like a new car.
It looks like a mole under the ground.
It sounds like a rock falling.

MY BEST DAY
My best day was when my Mam was having a baby in hospital and my Dad phoned and said that she had had a baby girl. And I remember the first time I saw her in the hospital. She was very chubby and she had long black hair and blue eyes. I was so happy it was a baby girl.

YELLOW
It is the moon in the dark, dark night.
It is a bright yellow banana.
It feels soft and slimy.

It is like a blob of paint falling.
It is the sound of an egg opening and the yolk falls out.

RAISIN
It is the smell of a new shoe.
It tastes a bit like honey on toast.
It feels like a squashy piece of leather.
It is the sound of pebbles falling onto other pebbles.
It is the look of rabbit poo.

THE BEST PERSON
My little sister, because she is my only sister and she is only one and she is really smart. I can remember the day she was born. I was so delighted that it was a baby girl, because now I would have a little sister to look after. And my little sister's name is Chloe, and that is why she is my best person.

CONFIRMATION HAIKU
Confirmation time
Is a time to prepare for
The Holy Spirit

AIR
Air is clear and mysterious.
You can't see it at all.
If there was no air we would not survive.
Air is gentle but can be powerful.

FIRE
Fire is hot like the bright sun.
It reminds me of Christmas Eve in the dark.
It smells like a burning forest.
Fire is like the burning ashes on Ash Wednesday.

Dylan Bradley

MY BEST DAY, MY WORST DAY
Best day was last Christmas because we got a new PC.
Worst day was when I got hit by a car when I was five.
Best day was when we went to Lanzarote.
Worst day was when I fell into the Mill River.
Best day was when I went skiing to Andorra.
Worst day was when my mum had to go to hospital and I thought she died.

Best day was when we got our new car.
Best day was when my Dad opened his new factory.
Worst day was the first day of school because I kept wanting to go home.
Best day is the day we get off school for summer holidays.
Best day was when we moved house from St. Mary Road to Railway Road.

RED

Red looks like a fatal disaster
Or just when your tooth comes out and your blood swirls around the sink.
It tastes like horrible sour milk put on cereal and shoved down your throat.
It feels like watery liquid that's thicker than water.

I AM

I am the day of my aunty's wedding.
I am the day the branch of our tree fell on our neighbour.
I am the day I made my Communion and got lots of money.
I am the day when me and my family collected my sister from the Gaeltacht.
I am the Christmas night my sister wouldn't stop getting me up in the middle of the night.
I am the car I liked most - our black car.

MY FIRST MEMORY

My first memory was when I was about three years old. I started my uncle's car. With a loud jump it sprang forward and hit the car in front of me. It jolted back and stopped. I was so frightened I could only sit there and stare blankly at the dent in the car in front of me. My mum ran out and tugged me out of the car and brought me inside.

BLUE

Blue is like the early school mornings.
It sounds like a messed-up job.
It tastes like a cold fizzy drink.
It smells like gas upon a stove.
It feels like velvety blue silk, suitable for kings.

GREY

Grey is the colour of dust from an attic.
Grey smells old like an ancient relic.
Grey feels like wool that has been tied into a hundred knots.
Grey is frustrating as trying to thread a needle.

SUGAR CRYSTAL

This small piece of jelly which has been burnt rock hard.

It looks like a rat's liver.
It tastes like sugar lumps stuck together.
It sounds like a rubber tyre skidding across gravel.

BRIDGES
Bridges represent
Hope to join us to unknown
Places and people

Mark Grant

MY BEST DAY, MY WORST DAY
My best day was when Liverpool won the FA cup in 1992, 2:0 against
Sunderland. I was cheering all day.
My worst day was when Manchester United beat Liverpool 1:0, four years
later. It was a very bad day, because people started taunting me and saying
support a real team.
My best day was when we had a sports day in school.
My worst day was when my daddy broke his arm when he fell off a roof.
My best day was when I almost won a writing competition.
My worst day was when I was sick and couldn't talk for three days.

GREEN
Green reminds me of trees blowing in the wind.
Green tastes like soup.
Green smells of freshly cut grass.
Green feels jaggy as if someone pokes your hand.
Green sounds like someone stamping their feet.

I AM
I am the day I got a pair of black and white shoes for a wedding.
I am the day I won a medal for football.
I am the day I first learned how to do joint writing. I was in third class.
I am the day I first learned how to count to a hundred.
I am the day I won an Easter egg.

MY PLACE IS
My place is the big P.E. hall at school.
My place is the leisure centre where there is a football pitch.
My place is the chapel where we go to pray.
My place is the way the water crashes against the rocks on a winter's evening.

My place is the shops and restaurants where there are good things to eat and buy.

WHITE
White is the colour of snow on a winter morning.
White feels soft.
White tastes like candy floss.
White sounds like the wind.
White looks like ghosts in a nightmare.

TIME HAIKU
While I sat I fell
I fell the way back in time
The dinosaurs cried

MY FIRST MEMORY
My first memory is my first day at school. I remember feeling nervous
going into a big school all alone. The teacher was telling me where to sit.
All the boys sat together and all the girls sat together. Some people were
crying and some people were laughing.

CURRANT
It reminds me of sultanas.
It sounds like gun caps only quieter.
It looks like a ruby from a ring.
It feels like catching the first hailstone that falls from the sky.

John Gill

MY BEST DAY, MY WORST DAY
My worst day was when I broke my arm.
My worst day is when we took the wrong road to Dublin.
My best day was when I got out of hospital.
My best day was when we got a new car.
My best day was when we were going to France.
My worst day was when I went up to theatre for my operation.

BARLEY
It smells like clove rocks.
It looks like sugar puffs.
When you drop it on the page it sounds like when you hit a golf ball with
a Big Bertha.
It is light green and white.

I don't know what it tastes like.

BROWN

Is the colour of a horse's mane.
It is a dead bush lying in the back of the garden.
It smells rotten.
It feels like dried-out muck falling through your hand.

I AM

I am the day my daddy got the new BMW.
I am the day I was out playing football when I saw a BMW going in the driveway
- I thought it was someone turning around but it wasn't, it was my daddy.
I am the day I was going down to somewhere with my Da. We had a big
trailer with us. We were getting a boat.
I am the morning I woke up from my operation. I was vomiting a wild lot.

MY PLACE IS

My place is the way Fruit of the Loom smells when you walk past it.
My place is the way our town is shaped.
My place is the way the water at the pier is very badly polluted.
My place is the way there is a wild lot of Council men and our town is
very dirty.

YELLOW

Yellow is like lemons in the supermarket.
It looks like the sand blowing across the beach.

Paul Deery

MY BEST DAY, MY WORST DAY

My best day was going to the beach and I stayed all day.
My worst day was when I was too tired to get up for school and missed my bus.
My best day was when I made my First Communion. We went out for dinner
after it.
My worst day was when I got hit three times on the face with a ball on my
birthday.
My best day was at my uncle's wedding and we stayed up late and got free drinks.
Best day was on Easter Sunday because I was off sweets for Lent and then
I ate a lot of sweets.

BLUE

Blue looks like the clear blue sky.
Blue smells of bluebells in the Spring.

Blue tastes of blue-mould bread after lying in the press.
Blue sounds of peace and quiet.

I AM
I am the day I made my Communion.
I am the day I lost my first tooth.
I am the day I learned how to ride my bike.
I am the day I got baptised.
I am the first day I went to school.
I am my first Christmas day.

MY FIRST MEMORY
My first memory was when I was four and I went on my holidays. We went to Bray. I remember going to see a sea-life exhibition. I remember going on a train. We stayed with my great grand aunty and her husband.

RED
Red is the colour you see when you cut yourself.
Red is the sound when something terrible happens.
Red feels like the soft skin on an apple.
Red is the colour that brightens the sky in the morning.

MY PLACE IS
My place is the way that school looks so dead on Saturday.
My place is the smell of dinner cooking in the house.
My place is the way the chapel is so alive on Sunday.
My place is the strong smell of salt at the beach.
My place is the way shops are more busy on a Saturday than on any other day.
My place is the smell of the chip shops when you go in to get something to eat.

FIRST THINGS
I tasted the warm tea I had for breakfast.
I heard the baby crying because he was hungry.
I could see my daddy rushing to get out because he had slept in.
I felt the warm water on my face as I was getting washed.

Gavin Bradley

I AM
I am the day I was born.
I am the day I got to be the page-boy at my aunty's wedding.

I am the day I got my play station for Christmas.
I am the day I went to work with my dad.
I am the day I made my first Communion.
I am the day of my parents' anniversary.

MY FIRST MEMORY

I remember my very first day at school. I fell off the chair and started to cry.
When it was play time I wouldn't let go of the door. I was afraid to go into
the playground. When school was over I ran out to my mum.

ORANGE

Orange is like a fire in the darkest room.
It tastes like a bitter fruit when you bite into it on a cold winter's day and
it numbs your teeth.
It reminds me of school.

MY PLACE IS

My place is the smell of the Fruit of the Loom.
My place is the beach with the beautiful sand.
My place is the football pitch.
My place is the street which is very dirty.
My place is the films at the cinema which come out a couple of months
after they come out everywhere else.

MY BEST DAY, MY WORST DAY

My worst day was when my baby cousin died the day after she was born.
My worst day was when the Omagh bomb went off.
My worst day was when my granda died.
My worst day was when I got stitches in my head.

BLACK

Black is like a dark room.
Black tastes like mints in your mouth.
Black feels like a rough piece of coal.
Black smells like burnt toast.
Black sounds like thunder.

WOOL

It looks a bit like my brother's pet chinchilla's fur.
It smells like a type of flower but I forget what type.
It sounds like a rough bit of cloth when you rub it.

Gary Grant

I AM
I am the day I put on my First Communion suit for the first time.
I am the time I went to the dentist for a check-up.
I am the day I went to my aunt's new home.
I am the time I split my head.
I am the time I split my cousin's head.
I am the first time I was at a funeral.
I am the day my parents crashed and I did not know what happened.

WOOL
This piece of wool reminds me of my granda. He was in the Red Cross. He lived in Toban with my granny. He died when I was eight years old. My granny is still alive. My piece of wool smells like oranges and it tastes like hair. It looks like a fake rat's tail.

MY PLACE IS
My place is the bedroom I sleep in. It is warm.
My place is when you pass you have to put up your window because it smells like a cowshed.
My place is the way my computer comes on.
My place is where I smashed a window on a motorbike.

MY FIRST MEMORY
I remember my first day at school. I was in Miss Sweeney's class. I was with all my friends and I did not cry. I did not have any books, only a school bag. My mummy did not stay.

BARLEY
It looks like a small piece of popcorn.
It makes the sound of Smarties.
It tastes like wood.
It looks a bit like bread.
It tastes like cardboard.

FIRST THINGS
This morning I tasted toothpaste.
I saw a pink car.
I smelled a cream egg.
I heard the speaker in O'Donnell's Supermarket.
I felt my sister's wig she had made for school.

SUGAR CRYSTAL
It tastes like sugar on your tongue.
It looks like crystal.
It's not hard to break.
It reminds me of the Marble Arch caves in Fermanagh.

Joseph Cullen

MY FIRST MEMORY
I remember the time I had my first operation. I was eating my dinner with my mother and then I think I got pains in my stomach, so we went to the doctors and we had to go to Letterkenny hospital and a couple of hours after that I was in for an emergency operation on my appendix. My other memory of this was the time I was allowed to eat food again. I had been on a drip. It was the most delicious tea and toast I ever had. I also got lemon things for my lips but I think I licked them.

I AM
I am the day I wore a waistcoat, shirt and trousers for my First Communion.
I am the day I made friends.
I am the day I went to my cousin's wedding.
I am the day I went to hospital.
I am the day the whole family went out for a meal.
I am the time I got home at 3 am.

RED
Red is the colour of red ink half used in a pen.
Red is when you see the sun setting in the evening. It looks like a red sky with the sun stuck in the middle and blinding you when you are trying to concentrate on it.
Red is the colour you see when you see cold blood.
Red is the look on everyone's face when the teacher gives a lot of homework.

MY PLACE IS
My place is the way the dung smells.
My place is the way the river keeps flowing.
My place is the way the cars go to and fro.
My place is the way the children keep playing in the boys' club.
My place is the way school seems so long.

MY BEST DAY, MY WORST DAY

My best day was when I started my StarWars collection.
My worst day was when I got a five on average.
My best day was going to Boston.
The worst day was when we saw our hotel room in the Isle of Man.
My worst day is when I don't know how to do sums.
My best day is when I do a good drawing.
My worst day is when I get scolded.
My worst day is when the best ones end.
My best day is when the worst ones end.

NAVY

Navy is the colour of Star Trek.
You mistake navy for black a lot.
Navy is undertaker from WWF.
Navy is the look on everyone's face if somebody dies.
Navy is the look on everyone's face if it's a school day.
Navy smells cold.

FIRST THINGS

I smelt the smell of paint because of decorating.
I felt the heat in my bed.
I saw the dim light because the curtains were closed.
I tasted the morning taste in my mouth.
I heard my mummy talking.
I saw the desk with my drawings on it.

Marguerite McLaughlin

MY FIRST MEMORY

My memory is when I was wee. My sister took her friend upstairs and left me downstairs, and I went up the stairs to her, crying. I was three and I felt very sad. I sat upstairs with them and I huffed when they told me to get out.

I used to annoy my mammy by scattering the dirt all over the floor when she brushed it up.

MY PLACE IS

My place is the way the waves crash against rocks on a stormy night.
My place is the delicious sweet smell of the bakers.
My place is the sound of the noisy trees and river when you walk around Swan Park.
My place is the feel of the sand when you walk on the beach at the shorefront.

My place is the bright sun shining on the picnic tables in the summer when you are having a picnic.

MY BEST DAY, MY WORST DAY
My best day was my tenth birthday when I went to the ice-rink and Barry's amusements.
My worst day was when I split my head on a swing.
My worst day was when I went to school for the first time.
My best day was when my nephews were born.
My worst day was when I got stuck up a tree in my aunty's house.
My worst day was the day my brother fell off a bridge in Dublin.

PURPLE
Purple feels like silk.
Tastes like chocolate.
Looks like a cosy room at night.
Smells like the smoke from candles.
Sounds like a small flame.

PINK
Is the colour of pigs.
It feels like a little girl's bedroom.
Pink smells like Calpol.
It looks like a sunny day.
It tastes like Cadbury's Roses.

DREAM
Beside my sister's house there is an old shed. Before she moved in, or even began to build the house, I had a dream about the shed. I was in it with my two sisters, looking for my granny, but my granny was not there. There are two rooms in it and my sisters went to one room and I went to another. I went to a chair that was turned towards the wall. When I looked at the chair the wall sucked me in. My sisters didn't notice I wasn't with them and they went on home. Then I woke up.

BRIDGE HAIKU
Bridges join people
Bridges make hope and love come
Bridges join us up

FIRST THINGS
I felt cold because my mum opened the window.
I saw the roof as soon as I woke up.
I heard my sister in a room rattling through drawers looking for her purse.
I smelt the smell of vanilla coming from my sister's candle that I lit last night.

The first thing I tasted was an egg for my breakfast.

Louise Doherty

I AM

I am the day of my first Holy Communion. I was very proud because I was wearing a long white dress.
I am the day I was flower girl for my aunty.
I am the day I fell and hurt my back. It was so painful.
I am the day I make my Confirmation.
I am the day my granda died.

MY PLACE IS

My place is the church beside our school.
My place is the very big beach.
My place is the sand soft and tickly.
My place is the rocks, very sharp and looking like high cliffs.
My place is the water sometimes looking a greeny bluey colour.

BRIDGES

Bridges feel very rough and jagged.
Very peaceful listening to the running water underneath.

FLINT

My stone feels rough and jagged.
It looks like there's sand in the middle of it.
If I taste it, it would probably break my teeth.
It reminds me of a big tall cliff.
It sounds like a hammer hammering nails into wood.

MY FIRST MEMORY

My first memory is going to the cinema with my mammy. I can't remember what was on. I remember the sound. It was so loud and it was very warm. Before we went in, my mammy bought me lots of sweets and they were lovely.

James Fullerton

MY BEST DAY, MY WORST DAY

My best day is getting off school for my summer holidays, or any other day that I get off school.
The worst day is going back to school after a holiday or a weekend.

My best day is my birthday because I get money and presents from my friends and relatives.

My worst day is when I have to turn the clock back and it gets dark earlier and I can't play football outside at night.

My best day is Christmas, Easter and Halloween, because at Christmas I get presents, on Easter I get Easter eggs and on Halloween I can stay up late.

My worst day is when a friend, relative, or person that I know, dies or goes to hospital.

My best day is when I go on holiday such as Andorra or Spain.

My worst day is when I break any part of my body. It is hard to run around or to play any sports.

My best day is when my teacher does not come to school and the class is split up into other classes.

My worst day is when our car will not start and I can't go to my cousin's house.

My best day is when we sell our old car and get a better one.

CLOVE
These smell of clove sweets that you can buy up the main street.
They sound like little drops of rain on a stony ground.
They feel jaggedy and rough.

PINK
Pink is the colour of happiness.
Pink tastes like little tablets from the Seven Seas.
Pink looks like the rough stuff on a rock.

MY FIRST MEMORY
I remember when I was in play-school eating lunch and the teacher was giving out biscuits and I was not allowed to get any. I was sitting on a toy tractor, eating my sandwiches and drinking Kulana orange juice.

I can remember going up to the hospital to see my baby brother, and my father was calling me to hurry, and he was up at the other side of the corridor calling me to come on.

I AM
I am the day I made my First Communion. I wore a blue shirt and a pair of shorts.
I am the day the Bradley family and my family went to Redcastle.
I am winning an Easter egg in fifth class.
I am the time I went to Killarney five years ago at Easter.
I am my first day at school, not letting go of my mother and crying.
I am the first friend I ever had - Dylan Bradley. He is still my friend.

MY PLACE IS

My place is the place that I love going to - Granny Fullerton's in Gransha.
My place is this town because lots of my cousins and friends and relatives live here.
My place is my bedroom.
My place is playing football and Gaelic on the Scarvey pitch.

VIOLET

Violet is the colour of love.
Violet smells of plums.
Violet sounds of rustling.
Violet tastes like jam.

Shaun Doherty

MY BEST DAY, MY WORST DAY

My best day is when we get out of school.
My worst day is going back to school after holidays.
My best day is on Christmas morning.
My worst day was when I broke my arm.
My best day was my first day going on holiday.
My worst day was when I split myself.
My best day was when United won the Premiership.
My worst day was hearing about the Omagh bomb.

RED

Red sounds like danger.
Red looks like blood when you get cut.
It feels smooth and valuable.
It smells like vodka.

MY FIRST MEMORY

My first memory was learning how to go on my bike. I didn't need stabilisers, and it took me about fifteen minutes. It was hard enough, but when I knew how to go, it wasn't so hard. Another of my memories was going to my first match in Tyrone: Donegal vs Tyrone, and Donegal beat them by sixteen points.

WOOL

It reminds me of my granny because she always knits jumpers.
It sort of feels tickly in your hand.
It looks like a tail.

I AM

I am the day I started school. I was terrified. I didn't want to go. I wanted
to stay at home and play with my toys.
I am the day I went on holidays. I was so excited, every so often I asked
my mum and dad *Are we there yet?*
I am the day I broke my arm. I was about four or five. My granda took me
a walk around the beach. I climbed the rock and fell and broke my arm.
I am the day my sister got an operation. My mum came in and woke me
up and got me to get changed. I was very worried because I didn't know
what had happened.

TURF

Turf smells like shoe polish.
It reminds me of the fire burning.
It sounds like a stone hitting an old wooden door.
It looks like pieces of dried-up muck and twigs.

BRIDGES

Bridges are a sign of peace and hope.
They join one place to another,
And they remind me of the worker trying to build them.

BRIDGES HAIKU

Bridges take you to
Different places in life.
They are important.

David Hone

MY BEST DAY, MY WORST DAY

My best day was the day that I came third in Antrim at running.
My worst day is back at school.
My other best thing is scoring goals at football.
My best thing is going to Blackpool for my holiday.
My best thing is I would like to go places.

CLOVE

It felt like a wee pebble.
It looks like popcorn seed.
It tastes like cloves.

MY FIRST MEMORY

My first memory was at a football match. It was filled with people and everybody was shouting and we were up in high seats and there were a lot of goals.

I AM

I am the day I wore my Man United top.
I am the day I was born.
I am the day I scored a goal.
I am the day I broke my arm.
I am the day when I ran.
I am the day I went to school.

Barry O'Loughlin

MY BEST DAY, MY WORST DAY

Best day was Christmas day 1998.
Best day was first day back at school.
Worst day was yesterday because we got a lot of homework.
Best day is Friday because no school the next day.
Worst day was when I fell and broke my wrist.
Best day was the day I got my wet suit.
Best day was when we got our new car.
Best day was when we went to Finn Valley with the school to do swimming.

CLOVE

They smell like riches.
They look like little stones you find on the beach.
There is no real sound to them.
They taste like riches.

RED

Red is the colour of Cadena's jumper.
Red tastes like blood in your mouth when you get punched.
Red feels very warm.

MY FIRST MEMORY

My first memory was when I was at a Gaelic match for the school. I broke my wrist. When I jumped up for the ball and came down, some boy stood on my hand. I got up and I couldn't move my hand.

I AM

I am Barry.
I am the day I was at a rally. It was very good. The cars were going very fast beside my friend Aidan's house.
I am the first night I had to work in Jimmy Grant's bar. I was very scared.

I am the day I got my Play Station.

MY PLACE IS
My place is Buncrana.
My place is the factory which went on fire one night.
My place is the beach which is wonderful in summer.
My place is the Pollim dam which has a lot of water.
My place is the way to Tipperary.

FIRST THINGS
I tasted my tea and toast.
I smelt my sister's perfume.
I saw my da work on the building site.
I heard cars and lorries going up and down the roads.
I felt my clothes going on.

POSTCARD
I am the dog in the picture. I can feel the fleas when one of these women pet me. I can hear the women roaring at one another. I am looking at a hot-dog cart. I can smell all those women's feet.

FLINT
It looks like a mountain very very very very far away.
On one side it is very smooth and on the other side it is very rough.
It was probably meant for cutting fish up.
It is very sharp around the edges.
It smells like it was on fire.

Laura Smith
PURPLE
It looks like grapes.
It feels like play dough.
It tastes like Ribena.
It reminds me of purple nail varnish.

MY PLACE IS
My place is school opening in the morning.
My place is the noise of it; children whispering or talking.
My place is the smell of people's lunches which they throw in the bin.
My place is the mixed colours of the notice-board.
My place is the windmill blowing in the wind.

MY BEST DAY, MY WORST DAY

My worst day is Monday because I have to get up early for school after the week-end.
My best day was when my sister was born because I had someone to play with.
My best day was when I made my first Holy Communion.
My worst day was the day of the Omagh bombing, because a lot of people died and a lot of people got hurt.
My worst day was when my uncle died.
My best day was when I got to the Community Games in Letterkenny.
My worst day was when my daddy was in hospital for Christmas.

CLOVE

It feels like tiny pebbles.
It looks like seeds from a sunflower.
I don't know what it smells like because I have a cold and my nose is blocked.

FIRST THINGS

I heard my alarm going off.
I smelt my uniform just out of the wash.
I saw the sun trying to come out.
I heard the birds outside my window.
I tasted my breakfast.
I smelt my toast burning because I forgot about it.

FLINT

As I am touching this stone I am wondering if somebody used it for killing animals years ago.
It feels very rough.
It sounds like very heavy hailstones banging off the car window.
It feels very jagged.
I wonder if somebody used it.
It looks like there are bits of glitter in it.

DREAM

I had a dream that I was in a restaurant called Food Heaven. I was very hungry and I had just ordered a big pile of food. I was just about to eat a big piece of chocolate cake when my mum woke me up and told me it was time to go to school.

BRIDGES

Bridges bring people together. They help us to get from one place to another. Shaun and his friends wrote a poem about building bridges and joining people together in peace. Bridges are a sign of hope.

Ciara McFeely

MY FIRST MEMORY
My memory is of when I got knocked down. I split my chin and the front
and back of my head. I felt uncomfortable and as if I was going to die. I
had stitches. I had a broken arm. I felt great after a few months.

WOOL
It smells like seats of a car.
It looks like a worm crawling out of the grass.
It feels like a bit of clothing.
It is grey and long.

I AM
I am the day when I made my First Communion. It was great.
I am the day when I first started school. I was scared.
I am the day I went to Belfast to see my sister. She got burnt by a kettle.
I am the day I got knocked down. Everyone was worried.
I am the day when I first went away to camp without my family.

GOLD
Gold reminds me of the sunset.
It feels like heat surrounding me.
It sounds like birds singing.
It smells like a winter flower.

FLINT
My stone feels like putting your hand in sand and rubbing it.

APRICOT
Is the apple that shines in my lunch box.
Is the colour of my bedroom.
Apricot sounds like trees rustling.
The sun rising.
It tastes like bits of fresh mint.

Óisín Ó Flaithbheartaigh

TURF
Turf is in the bog.
Turf - when it's in the fire it is red.
It's like thunder when you bang it on the table.
You need turf for the fire.

MY PLACE
Is the club.
Is the way you can play: football; pool; squash and table tennis.

MY BEST DAY, MY WORST DAY
My best day was in Old Trafford.
My best day was meeting all the football players.
My worst day is when we get a lot of homework.
My best day is getting off school for two months.
My worst day is going back to school.
My best day is when we went on holiday to Orlando, Florida.

BARLEY
They look like seeds.
It sounds like rain.
It is like hailstones when you throw a few at the page.

BLACK
Reminds me of school.

THOUGHT
Fire
Warm
Sticks
I do not know where
I am from

DREAM
I have a dream to play for my country and Man Utd. To play in Wembley
Stadium. To beat England in the World Cup Final. To beat Arsenal in the FA
Cup Final, and I score the goal. To get player of the year over and over again.
And to be the best player in the world.

SCHOOL HAIKU
It is Friday yes
My best ever day thank god
No school then ha ha.

Michael Hegarty

MY FIRST MEMORY
My first thing I remember is in Derry, shopping. For me it felt good. My

mammy and daddy were there. It was a good day.

WOOL
It looks like my school jumper.
It smells like moth-balls.
It reminds me of a rat's tail.

I AM
I am the day I was born.
I am the day I was Baptised.
I am the day I wore my new shoes.
I am the day I played golf.
I am the day I drew a picture.

GREEN
Looks like an apple when someone is eating it.

MY BEST DAY, MY WORST DAY
My best day was jumping off the pier.
My best day was winning the football match in Derry.
My worst day was losing the football match at Finn Valley.
My best day was going on holiday to Portugal.
My worst day was coming home from holiday.
My best day was going on my school tour to the zoo.

POSTCARD
I am a dog in Greece. I am going for a walk. My owner will not take me because he is too busy in the shop with no customers.

YELLOW
Yellow, because it is very lucky.
It smells like the sun on a warm day.
It feels like a bright taste - like yoghurt.
Yellow looks like dandelions.

SUGAR CRYSTAL
It looks like a Cola bottle.

TEN WORDS FOR A DESERT ISLAND
Peace; Food; Football; Golf; Joy; Happiness; Goodness; Friend; Holy; Money.

Caroline Forshaw

MY FIRST MEMORY
I remember I was in my cot. I was a babby. It smelt like apple. I was about one. I was playing with my doll. I called her Elaine. Everywhere I went, she came too. One day I went to the shop. I forgot her. I began to cry and mummy had to go home and get her.

I AM
I am the night I got lost. It was a wet night.
I am the runners I got which were too small for me.
I am the day I got my wet suit.
I am the day I got a dress for my birthday.
I am the day I went on my holidays. It was good.
I am the first day I went to school.
I am the day I got scolded by the teacher.

BLUE
It tastes like blueberries.
It looks like a big blue room.
It sounds like standing on a sledge.

MY BEST DAY, MY WORST DAY
My best day was when I got my wet suit.
My worst day was when I ripped my wet suit.
My worst day was when I fell off the pier.
My best day was when my aunt got married.
My worst day was when I split my head in the pool.
My best day was when I went horse-riding.
My worst day was when I fell off the horse.

FLINT
My stone looks like a Christmas tree.
It sounds like glass when you drop it.

RED
Red is the colour when I cut my knee.
Red smells like a rose.
Red, red is red.
Red sounds like blood dripping off your knee.

DREAM

It was all about horses. I was on a horse. I was on the St. Patrick's ride. We had a competition as to who would be the best on the horse from Inch stables to the town, and when we got back to Inch, Jane told me that I had won. I was over the moon. Mum woke me up.

Tara Mullan

MY FIRST MEMORY

My first memory is when I was a baby and my cousins always took me out for walks. They would take me to the shops and my granny's. I loved the fresh air and the wind.

WOOL

It reminds me of the wool of the sheep on the barbed wire.

I AM

I am the night of a big storm.
I am the day I went shopping in Derry.
I am the day I woke up early in the morning.
I am the day I heard a noise outside.
I am the day I went swimming with my family.

BARLEY

It reminds me of bones.
It is the colour of skin.

LILAC

Smells like clothes coming out from the dryer.

TURF

It feels rough on your hands.
It reminds me of spiders.
When you drop it, it sounds like a dice rolling in a game.

MY PLACE IS

The way the pictures open at a certain time.
My place is the way the colour of the sea water is deep blue.
My place is the smell of the factory when you walk past.

MY BEST DAY, MY WORST DAY

My best day was when I got a baby sister. Mummy fed her and cleaned her and I would help. I loved helping mummy with the baby.

My worst day was when it was raining and I couldn't go outside. It never stopped raining. It rained all day. I had to sit inside looking out the window.
My worst day was when I heard about the Omagh bombing.
My best day was when I came first in a karate competition.
My worst day was when I fell and hurt myself.
My best day was when I went to Croagh Park.

RED
Reminds me of ladybirds.

GOLD
Reminds me of coins.
It smells like iron.

DREAM
I had a dream that I was stranded in a desert by myself and nobody was there. I was thirsty and hungry and I had nothing with me. It was very warm and I needed a drink. Then I saw an oasis. I was running towards it but then I woke up in my own bed.

David McLaughlin

MY FIRST MEMORY
I was two. I was going on my holidays to Spain. It was very hot.

WOOL
It looks like sheep's hair.
Bear hair.
Rat tail.

I AM
The day of the summer holidays.
I am the day of my birthday.
I am the day of the match.
I am the day of Óisín's daddy's death.

MY BEST DAY, MY WORST DAY
My best day is the 24/8/99, my birthday.
My worst day is the 1st September, when we go back to school.
My best day is going to a wedding.
My best day is the first day of the summer holidays.
My worst day is 15/8/98 when Shaun died.
My worst day was when my daddy was in a car crash.

GREEN
Green is like apple tart.
It looks like a green car.

DREAM
One night I was driving the car and I was going up the road.

TIME
In half an hour's time it will be 11 am - our break.
In two hours' time it will be twelve thirty - our lunch.
In four-and-a-half hours' time it will be 3pm - home time.
In seven-and-a-half hours' time it will be 6pm - dinner.

Padraic McLaughlin

MY FIRST MEMORY
My first memory is when I went over to Leeds and watched Leeds play
Chelsea. The score was 0-0. I also remember going to the training ground and
watching them train. I remember getting a tour of the ground and meeting all
the players.

WOOL
It looks like a shoe-lace.

YELLOW
Yellow is like the sand on the beach.
It smells like paper.
It looks like the corn blowing in the field.

TURF
This thing reminds me of the bog.
It looks like a dead mouse squashed up on the ground.
It smells like the bark of a tree.
It sounds like heavy rain hitting off a roof.
It looks like the colour of a dark sky.

MY PLACE IS
My place is the smell of the dye in the factory.
My place is the goal posts in the Gaelic pitch as they lurk up into the air.
My place is the way the river flows past the rocks and trees in Swan Park.
My place is the way the farmers are out working in the fields.
My place is the way the windmills swirl around up in the Illies.

MY BEST DAY, MY WORST DAY

My best day was on Christmas morning last year when I went downstairs and got all my things.

My worst day is when we got beaten in the final of the Inishowen Cup against Clonmany.

My second best day is when Donegal won the Sam Maguire cup. They beat Dublin in the final.

My worst day was when my cousin died in the Omagh bomb.

BARLEY

It looks like the seed out of an orange.
It reminds me of the things that are in vegetable soup.

FIRST THINGS

I smelt smoke on the way to school.
I heard birds singing in the air.
I saw the steam coming out of the chimney of the factory.
I heard the cars going down the road.
I felt the wall when I got up.

FLINT

It looks a bit like marble.
It sounds like horses' feet hitting off the tarmac.
It has a sharp pointy edge on it like a knife.

GOLD

Gold is the colour at the end of the rainbow.
Gold is very rich.
Gold reminds me of the World Cup.

Bridgeen Morrison

MY FIRST MEMORY

I am sitting out the back of the house with my friend and we sat in a basin of water.

I went on a tour to Omagh with my Spanish friends.

WOOL

It feels like a furry animal I had petted when I was on a school tour.
It looks like the wool we saw when we were in the Ulster American Folk Park.

I AM

I am the day I went to Omagh on 15th August and a bomb went off and it was a long bang.
I am the day I wore a purple dress.
I am the day I went with the school to Omagh on a fun day.
I am the day I went to a Boyzone concert.

BLUE

Blue is the colour that your face goes when something gets stuck in your throat.
Blue tastes like bubble gum.
Blue looks like the daylight sky.
Blue is the colour of my lunch-box.

MY PLACE IS

My place is the river in Buncrana.
My place is the way I know our town - it is magic.
My place is the way I know the beach at Buncrana.
My place is the way my house is built in a park.
My place is the way the streets of Buncrana are long and narrow.

MY BEST DAY, MY WORST DAY

My worst day was when I was in Omagh on 15th August.
My best day was when my mum got on the millionaire show.
My worst day was when I fell off my bike.
My best day was when I went to my friend's party in Derry.
My best day was the Spanish coming to Ireland.
My worst day was when everyone was fighting with me.

BLACK

Like the smoke from the fire.
Black, like my room at night when the light isn't on.
Black, like the colour of my best friend's hair.

BRIDGES

Bridges remind me of Shaun's peace poem, and of the song *Across the Bridge of Hope*. I like to cross bridges.

BRIDGE HAIKU

Bridges need to be
Crossed from one to another
Or else we don't move

Cadena Doherty

MY FIRST MEMORY

My first memory is when I was three and I fell and cut my knee which was a really deep cut. It was really sore, and there was blood everywhere. I remember getting it cleaned out, and it was really stinging. I got stitches in it. There was a scar on my leg from then on. I got a sticker from the doctor.

My other memory was when I fell off a see-saw and sprained my wrist. I couldn't lift anything with my right hand for quite a while. I remember getting a bandage on it.

WOOL

It feels like wool and it looks like the colour of the grey sky on a winter's day. It has no sound - it is silent, which is like when you walk into a chapel and it is quiet.
It smells like the smell you get when you walk into an old shop.

I AM

I am the day when I wore a little dress and hat to my cousin's wedding.
I am the day I went to the zoo.
I am the day I made my Communion and wore a long white dress with silk gloves and a little bag.
I am the day I got my dog and it was just a little pup and it was really small and when it went outside to play it made a squeak and he was trying to bark.
I am the day I went to my cousin's christening and she was wearing a long silk dress, and cried while being christened.
I am the day I played my first Gaelic match.

GREEN

Green looks like a cabbage.
Green feels like a leaf on the tree.
Green sounds like grass crunching.

MY PLACE IS

My place is the way the trees cover the back garden.
My place is the way you can hear the sea waves crashing on the rocks in the distant waters.
My place is the smell of the factories.
My place is the way you can see the boats fishing on the far side of the water.
My place is the way you can hear the noise of the cars on the road.
My place is the way you can see the mist settling over the faraway hills.
My place is the way you can hear the children playing.

MY BEST DAY, MY WORST DAY

Worst day was a stormy day when a tree fell on our garden.
Best day was when I got my dog.
Best day was when I moved house.
Worst day was when my granny got ill.
Worst day was when my uncle died.
Worst day was when my dog went missing.
Best day was when I went on a school tour to the Marble Arch caves.
Worst day was when my godmother went to Australia.

FLINT

It sounds like a marble hitting another marble.

BRIDGES

I've seen the bridge at Swan Park which you can walk on and look down upon the water.

Siobhán McLaughlin

FIRST MEMORY

My first memory was when I was three years old and I was copying my brother, and a chip pan fell on top of me and my neck was burned and I was rushed to hospital.

WOOL

It looks like an old person's hair.
It reminds me of an iron jumper.

I AM

The day I was a flower-girl at my uncle's wedding.
The day I started school.
I am the day I made my Communion.
I am the day I went to England.
I am the day I went to a Boyzone concert.

TURF

Reminds me of the country, the fire and the farmers out working on the hillside.
It smells like clay.
It makes a thumping sound.

MY BEST DAY, MY WORST DAY

My best day was when I made my First Communion. I was six years old and had long curly hair. I was wearing a big white dress. I made my First

Communion in St. Mary's Oratory. My parents, my sister, my brother and my granny was there. We went out for a meal afterwards to Ballyliffen Hotel. The priests that were there were Father Paul and Father Ciaran.

My worst day was when I was at the beach in Portaw with my sister and my three cousins. It was in the summer and we had got our swimming suits on. We got into the water and it was freezing. We got out again and it started to rain and later it started to thunder. We packed up and went home.

BLUE
Reminds me of the sky in a hot country and it sounds like the sea.

FIRST THINGS
When I got up I touched my dog.
I tasted the toothpaste when I was brushing my teeth.
I saw my school uniform folded on a chair.
I heard my dog barking to get out.

GOLD
It looks like rings and chains.
It smells like a posh person's house.
It sounds like famous bands.

DREAM
I had a dream about somebody I knew who went into space. The spaceship ran out of fuel and went too near the sun. They all got burned.

Brendan McCallion

MY FIRST MEMORY
My first memory was when I got lost in Galway. I walked out of a shop that my mammy was in. She was very worried. I was very sad. She found me after a while. I was glad to see her. She was very angry.
My second memory is going to school on my first day. I did not want to leave my parents but I was forced. Later in the day the teacher let us draw. The day was not so bad because when I got home I told everyone all about it.

WOOL
Looks like small, forged strands of metal winding together.
It smells like it has been in a dark place for a long time.

I AM

I am the day I went to see Andy Cole. The amount of people was unbelievable. The crowd lined up to see him.
I am the day my cousin got knocked down and everybody was worried.
I am the day the sheep knocked me down and I hurt my leg.
I am the day when my cousin broke her arm.
I am the day when I came home from school and my mummy had soup ready for me.

BARLEY

It feels rough and hard on my hand.
It reminds me of porridge in my granny's house.

NAVY

Navy looks like a policeman's uniform.
Navy is the colour of a dark road in the evening.
Navy looks like the roof of a new house.
Navy reminds me of a King's robe.

FLINT

My object has been hoisted up from a deep dark hole in the ground.
It sounds like a woodpecker knocking at a tree when it drops on my page.

MY BEST DAY, MY WORST DAY

My best day was when I was playing with my cousins in Galway.
My best day was when my uncle opened Abrakebabra.
Best day was when my cousins came from New Zealand.
Worst day was when my cousins went back to New Zealand.
Worst day was coming from France on the boat.
Worst day was the day of the storm.
Worst day was when my granny died.

GREEN

Green is the colour of Christmas

FIRST THINGS

When I got up this morning I smelt the fresh air.
When I went onto my bus I tasted the dust in the back of my throat.
When I got to the school I saw all my friends.
When I got inside I felt my hand gripping my pen.

SILVER

Silver is moulding metal.

65

Silver is glitter.
Silver is sparkling water.
Silver is shiny new cars.
Silver is the Tin Man from the Wizard of Oz.

BRIDGES

Bridges come in different shapes.
Some of them are over seas
And some of them are over lakes:
Some are big and some are small
Some are short and some are tall
Some are blue and some are green
Some look nice and some look mean.

Roy Gamble

FIRST MEMORY

My first memory is about three years ago, I was in a car crash. I had to stay in the hospital for one night.

RED

Red looks like a ladybird.
Red is a bull that is very mad.

MY PLACE IS

My place is the way that there is always a smell of fields.
The clock we have is an hour wrong.

MY BEST DAY, MY WORST DAY

My best day was last Christmas.
My worst day was when I was in a car crash.
The worst day was when my granny died.
Worst day was when I came home and my mum had fallen off the roof.

POSTCARD

I feel really happy and I am thinking about ships at sea.

DREAM

That I was in the USA. I had a dream that I was in the car and the car was about to crash, and then I was in a big dark room.

Graeme Rutledge

MY FIRST MEMORY
My first memory was when I got hit by a scythe. I was walking behind my dad and he could not see me. He hit me with the back of it. I kept on bleeding for ages.

WOOL
It reminds me of our neighbour's Collie pup. Its fur was wiry. It smells like a dog.

MY PLACE IS
My place is the house that has a sea view.
My place is the house that I live in - it always seems quiet.
My place is the house that catches the wind.

MY BEST DAY, MY WORST DAY
My best day was when I went to Warwick and we went to the castle.
The worst day was when I had measles.
My best day was when I went to London to see Madam Tussaud's Wax Museum.
My worst day was when we were coming back from Jersey. We were flying through a storm.

POSTCARD
I am really relaxed. There is nothing on my mind. I am in a cafè in Greece. I am sitting outside and there is a warm breeze blowing. I am waiting to be served. I think I might sit here all day.

STONE
When you drop it on the table it reminds me of a blacksmith.

DREAM
That I was in a rainforest. I could hear birds singing and monkeys howling. We were looking for tropical parrots. A mountain gorilla came chasing after us. We fell off the edge of a cliff. Then I woke up at the bottom of the bed.

BRIDGE
The bridge joins one place to another.
Its arches are dark and gloomy.
A fisherman was fishing in a shallow pool.
It is made of old stone.
There is ivy growing on one side.
The arch reminds me of a porch of a Cathedral.

Ian Ferguson

MY FIRST MEMORY
My first memory was when I went to an air show with my mammy and daddy, and the planes were trying to shoot at a bouncy castle.

RED
It sounds like the petals of roses blowing in the wind.

TURF
It smells like smoke.

MY PLACE IS
The house that I live in is very noisy.
My place is the countryside that has lots of animals.
My place is the countryside which is very smelly.

MY BEST DAY, MY WORST DAY
My best day was when I went on holiday.
My worst day was when I split my head off a door.
My best day was when we got our new dog.
My worst day was when I got stitches in my head.

DREAM
I had a dream that I was a cat and that I had to eat cat food and mice all day.

BRIDGE
Bridges are so big
They let you across water
Without getting wet.

Farren McDonald

MY FIRST MEMORY
My first memory was getting a dog which I still have. Around the same time we had a car crash.

WOOL
It feels rough and I can't hear anything coming from it but it reminds me of sheep and my grandad's hair.

ORANGE
Orange feels squishy.

It tastes like a melting ice-lolly.
It sounds like the sea in Spain.

TURF
It looks like a small island from a great distance.

MY PLACE IS
My place is the house where I live. It always seems to catch the light.
My place is the road beside my house which is broken and cracked.
My place is the dog that I own. He is fat and lazy and seems to block out the sun.
My place is the church down the road. It always feels cold.

MY BEST DAY, MY WORST DAY
My worst day was almost getting hit by lightning.
My best day was Christmas '95.
My worst day was when my granny died.

BARLEY
It looks like a bug or a beetle.
It sounds like a mouse running.

PURPLE
Purple tastes like blackcurrants.
Purple feels like sponge.
Purple sounds like bouncy balls bouncing.
Purple looks like a cold swamp.

FLINT
Small rock, big and hard.
It look like ice-berg.
Me no see ice-berg.
Me only see big rock - big rock hard.
It smell like fire.
Me make kill deer tool of it.
It sound like bowling ball.
It taste like limestone.

TIME
I am iron master
Of time. I don't know how I
Made this haiku rhyme.

BRIDGE
A bridge links one place to another.

Without it we'd have to swim.
We'd get all wet and bitten by fish.
There'd be sewage and dirt and you could catch a disease and die.

Leeann McLaughlin

I AM
I am the day of the Boyzone concert.
I am the memory of our friends who were killed last summer.
I am the time my grandad taught me poems.
I am the memory of when I would not go to sleep unless someone would read me the story Bambi.
I am the band I like best - Boyzone.

MY PLACE IS
My place is the big rocks standing still on the high hill.
My place is the beams of light that filter through the trees.
My place is the lovely sound of peacefulness and quietness.
My place is the way you feel like you are on top of the world when you get to the top.
My place is the way the animals quietly go about their business.

MUSIC
It reminds me of standing at the grave on my grandad's funeral, there were people crying all around me and even though I was young the sadness was building up in me. It reminds me of standing at the grave of Shaun, Oran and James's funeral as well.
It sounds like someone is trying to get a message through but no-one is listening. It makes me feel sad inside because it makes me think of my dead friends and family, especially my grandas and our friends who were killed in Omagh last summer. And this song makes me think of these tragic days.

MY FIRST MEMORY
I remember when one day my mammy had to go away for a while so my grandad had to come up and look after me. I was bored so he lifted me up on his knee and started to tell me poems such as *Hickory Dickory Dock* and *Jack and Jill*. He taught me about five nursery rhymes that day but the one I remember most would be *Hickory Dickory Dock*. For weeks after I could not stop saying the poem. He died when I was about five or so but I always think of my granda when I hear the poems.

EGG

The egg wobbles like jelly when you shake the plate.
Part of the egg split and there is some orange yolk around the rim.
The white of the egg is turning yellow just like the edge of the burning sun.
The egg shell smells like the chicken barn it came out of.
The shell reminds me of young children gathering shells on the beach.
The orange bit has split and one bit is covering another like the clouds on the moon.
The egg's fortune could be something to do with splitting up.

STONE

It smells like clove rock.
It looks like a grey ocean which has started to sparkle with gold.
It sounds like small marbles rolling across the table.
It feels like the pointy edges of broken glass.
It looks like the lifeless colour of death and the brown is the coffin around it.
It reminds me of a big rock being slowly covered with water.

RED

Red looks like burning flames in a dark room.
Red smells like the fumes of burning fire.
Red feels like when you put your hand on the blood of a cut.
Red sounds like someone calling where no-one can hear them.
Red tastes like a very hot sweet stinging your tongue.

AIR

Air looks like the sheep moving swiftly over the hill.
Air feels like the gale force wind blowing right in my face.
Air tastes like cold ice-cream when it hits sensitive teeth.
Air sounds like the whirl of the breeze outside.
Air smells like the spring has come too soon or too late.
Air reminds me of the wrinkly waves drifting out to sea.
Air keeps us alive in our world.

MY WORST DAY

One of the worst days of my life was when my granda died and his funeral was bad too. I remember I had been very close to him, and when he was being buried I was crying, even though I was quite young. I remember it was raining when he was being buried, but when we came home for tea with people from the funeral, it was a lovely day then. I miss him very much.

FIRE

The flame grows higher and higher as the candle becomes used to having

a flame flicker out of the top of it.
The flame stands still and then quickly flickers to one side.
It makes me think of a proud soldier standing still on the hilltop.
When breath touches it, it sways slowly to and fro.
It reminds me of watching the burning flames when the lights go out,
because there is nothing better to do.

Oran McLaughlin

I AM
I am the day I went to Brussels with my family.
I am the day I went to school.
I am the day I made my First Communion.
I am the day when I first went to the swimming pool.
I am the day I went to hospital for my operation.
I am the day I went to Spain with my family.
I am the day my grandad died.

MY FIRST MEMORY
I remember when I was three my family and I moved to Brussels. We stayed
there for six months. Every night an ice-cream van came and I would always
get one. After a month a funfair came and I went there every week. My
granny and aunty came and they stayed with us for two weeks. An old lady
lived in the room beside us. She would take me into her room to watch her
T.V. and eat some ice gems.

MY PLACE IS
My place is the back yard where I play and have a bar-b-que in the summer.
My place is the room where I sleep and read books.
My place is the view outside my window.
My place is the field across from my house where I make huts with my friends.
My place is the shore front where the fireworks go off in the music festival.

MY WORST DAY
My worst day was the day of the Omagh bombing. One of my friends died. My
Spanish student was very badly injured. Everyone in Buncrana was very sad.

AIR
It sounds like someone whistling.
It looks like lines drawn on a piece of paper.
It tastes like a tune.

It feels cold and like a fan blowing in your face.
It feels like your chest going in and out when you breathe.
It looks like someone blowing a fire with bellows.

EGG
It feels like a soft slimy substance.
It looks like the sun or a yellow blob of paint.
It smells like a dog.
It feels like water.
It sounds like a window cracking when the shell is opened.
It tastes lovely when scrambled.
Its yolk feels like paint.

RED
Red smells like jam.
Red looks like blood.
Red sounds like the ambulance.
Red feels like a soft tomato.

HAY
It feels like hair when you put hairspray on it.
It smells like grass.
It sounds like quiet footsteps.

FIRE
When it's lit, a poof of smoke rises into the air.
You can feel heat when you put your hand above it.
It makes me think about heat.
It makes me think about death.
It is a nice warm sunny feeling.
It looks like gold.
It's the Holy Spirit.

WATER
It's clear and cold.
It tastes like a spring.
It's soft.
It gives life.
It can cause death.

Joseph Friel

I AM
I am the nest that is still on the tree outside the classroom.
I am the day I made my Communion.

I am the day I started school.
I am the day I got baptised.
I am the day I started to walk.
I am the day I left Ireland and went to England.
I am the day I came back to Ireland.

MY PLACE IS

My place is the way the silence surrounds me.
My place is the way the roads lead me into nowhere.
My place is the way the air surrounds me.
My place is the way to get away.

MY WORST DAY

The worst day of my life was when my Mum died. My Dad phoned an
ambulance and my sisters and my brother were crying.

DREAM

I dreamt I walked into the classroom and everyone shot me. Then I got up
and everyone jumped out the windows and most of them fainted, and the
teacher ran out screaming.

FIRST THINGS

I heard the birds singing.
I tasted my cereal.
I felt the spoon.
I smelt bacon and eggs.
I saw the door.
I saw the dog playing with the cat.
I felt someone hitting the back of my head on the school bus, then someone
kicked me.

RED

Red looks like blood.
It tastes like chilli.
It sounds like a volcano erupting.
It smells like paint.
And worst of all it feels like nothing.

Christopher McDermott

I AM

I am the day I made my Communion.
I am the day I started school.

I am the day I split my head.
I am the day my Granda died.
I am the day my Mammy was sick.
I am the day I came back from Dublin.

BLACK

Black looks very scary.
It smells very poisonous.
It feels dark.
It sounds like something is going to happen.
It tastes like the moon.

MY PLACE IS

My place is my garage roof: the wood is very safe.
My place is the bar on the roof where we swing from.
My place is the best fun.
My place is the two people who know about it - my friend and I.
My place, the roof, is very dusty.

FIRST THINGS

When I woke up this morning I heard birds.
I saw my daddy leave for work.
And I smelled my breakfast.
Then I tasted my tea and toast.
I felt sore when the boys started to hit me.
I felt happy when we had creative writing.

AIR

Air sounds like someone speaking.
It feels like someone is breathing into you.
You can't see the wind.
Air is good for you.

FIRE

It makes me think about the Omagh bomb.
It feels hot and dangerous.
It has a bad smell.
It can kill you.
So can the smoke.
It is a very dangerous weapon.

EARTH

It feels like wet clay.
It reminds me of the old days.

It makes me think about my old tractor.

HAY
It feels like a spider coming up your neck.

Keara Barr

I AM
I am the day I started school. My teacher was Mrs. Sweeney.
I am the day I meet my best friend Laura.
I am the day I made my First Communion.
I am the day I went to America.
I am the day I went to Portugal.
I am the day my daddy and mammy got married. I was a flower-girl.

MY WORST DAY
The worst day of my life was when my Uncle moved to Australia and I never saw him until he came to visit us when I was eight. He brought my cousin too and I haven't seen him since then. My mammy was glad to see him. He stayed in my house for two days but he had to go home three days after.

MY PLACE IS
My place is the way my room looks when it is a mess.
My place is the way my mother shouts at me.
My place is the way my daddy is at work all the time.
My place is the way I wake up in the morning.
My place is the house I live in.

MY FIRST MEMORY
I remember when I made my First Communion. It was a windy day. I had my hair done up and when I got into the church I saw my friend Michelle was behind me and I think Laura was in front of me and the priest made us walk around the church. My mammy, daddy, granda and granny were there. Some of my aunties and uncles and cousins were there. We went to the White Strand after and we spent all day there.

EARTH
It has no smell.
It feels cold.
It sounds like little drops of rain.
It looks like muck.

It reminds me of my granda's farm.

Kathryn McColgan

DREAM

It was about my aunt. And she had gone out. And on the way back a car had knocked her down and she was dead. Then my uncle came to tell us. And he went to look for the people who did it and left her to die. It happened when I was down in my granny's and the dream took place in my granny's. When I woke up I told my granny and she said that a robin flew in the window the day before and that meant speedy news and dreaming about the dead was unlucky. Then the phone rang and the aunt had been rushed in to hospital.

MY PLACE IS

My place is the water is blue.
My place is the way the tide goes in and out.
My place is the sand.
My place is the way we go in the summer evenings.

AIR

Air is invisible but there.
Air is life.
Air is warm and so cold.
Air is untouchable.
Air is growth.

WATER

It made my hand look very far away.
It is cold.
We need water to live.
Water is clear and pure.

HAY

It looks like grass.
It feels like sewing thread.
It smells like nothing.
It sounds like air when it falls.
It tastes empty and tasteless.

MISSING HAIKU

We miss you so much
We never thought you would go
I will see you soon

Orla O'Donnell

I AM
I am the day I made my first Holy Communion.
I am the day I first started school.
I am the summer holiday.
I am the day the Omagh bomb went off and our friend died.
I am the first time I went swimming. I nearly drowned.
I am the day I did bridesmaid for Bride of the Year, my cousin.

MISSING
The boy went missing
In the shopping mall today.
His name was Jamie.

DREAM
I once had a nightmare that my house went on fire. I got out but my family didn't get out. I lost everything; my mum, dad, brothers and sisters. All my clothes and things. I was so sad. I went to stay with my aunt. When I woke up I was so scared that night that the house was really going to go on fire, that I stayed awake that whole night.

FIRE
It smells like firelighters.
It is red, orange and yellow.
It makes me think about a house on fire and people trapped inside.
Fire is a terrible way to die.
Fire is the sign of light.

AIR
It tastes like the bitter fruit.
It smells like a summer's day.
Without air I would die.

WHITE
It feels like cold ice.
It looks like a bright light.
It sounds like sugar and teeth chattering.
It smells minty.

EGG
It looks like a flying saucer.

MY FIRST MEMORY
I remember when I was two years old, I had to go hospital because I dehydrated. My brother had also dehydrated and had to go to hospital. I didn't think

it fair because my brother got a double bed and I got a cot. I remember there was a door in front of me and one day my Mum and Dad, brothers, sisters, Aunt Josie and Uncle John and their children, came. Every time the door opened, I would shout *Mummy* and *Daddy*.

Aileen Henerson

I AM
I am the time I made my Communion.
I am the time I started school.
I am the park where I played when I was little.
I am the time when my grandad died.
I am the time I went to America.

MY PLACE IS
My place is the flowers shooting up in the springtime.
My place is the river rippling beside you as you walk.
My place is the trees with their bark so brown.
My place is the plaques with the prints of flowers and leaves.
My place is the Castle bridge with the six arches.
My place is Swan Park.

DREAM
Once, every night before I went to the dentist, I used to have a nightmare that my teeth were stuck together and I used to wake up screaming. That was because I didn't like going to the dentist. Back then I thought it was really scary, and that when I woke up it would be real, but looking back it was stupid really.

AIR
Air is life on a spring day.
Air sounds like the silence in my room.
Air smells like the beach.
Air looks like the blue sky above you.

PURPLE
Purple is the colour in the rainbow.
It's what the sunset looks like.
It is the smell of the crocus.
It tastes like round grapes and plums.
It is the colour of death.

MY BEST DAY

My best day was the day I went to America. I couldn't wait. We left on a bus to Dublin at twelve o'clock at night. We were four hours on the bus and I was really tired but I couldn't sleep. When we got to Dublin Airport it was chaos. Everyone was looking for their cases and it was raining. When we were inside we got a cup of tea to get warmed up and then we went to the Duty Free. When it was time to get on the plane I was even more excited. During the journey, when you looked out the window you were so high that you could only see the blue sky. When at last we got there, it was beautiful and I was very jet-lagged, but I didn't care. I loved being in America.

Denise Doherty

I AM

I am the day I made my Communion.
I am the evening I watched my granny baking.
I am the day we got no homework.
I am Christmas morning.
I am the day I started school.
I am the day I went to Scotland.
I am the day my aunty had a baby.

MY FIRST MEMORY

My memories are of my granda. His name is Eamon. He always had a smile and never sad. He would have gone to golf every Wednesday and Saturday mornings. He would have watched golf every day and it would be the only thing he would watch. He had very bad chest problems and had a nebuliser and two inhalers. He died on 18th May, 1994. That is my memories of my grandad.

MY PLACE IS

My place is the soup that my granny makes.
My place is the smell that's in my granny's.
My place is the warmness of the radiators.
My place is the bedroom that is warm.
My place is the size of my granny's house.
My place is the furniture in my granny's room.
My place is the carpets that are new.
My place is where the curtains hang down.
My place is where the sun reflects in.

DREAM
I had a dream that one morning I was clerking Mass and I was the only one there. Then the next thing somebody came down from heaven to the chapel. I heard some noises from up above. I looked up and I saw a boy who was Shaun. He came down and helped me clerk. I was so glad to see him. He was telling me about the bomb in Omagh. I woke up crying.

Gary Coughlan

MY FIRST MEMORY
I was in High Infants. My friend and I were playing golf on the local football field. It was his shot and I was behind him when he swung. He hit me right above my eye. His mother tried to tell him to stop but he didn't. I had to get seven stitches. I made a friend in the hospital. He had got hit by a car. My mother visited me every day.

I AM
I am the day my grandad died.
I am the day I made my Communion.
I am the day I got a hernia operation.
I am the two times I moved house and county.
I am the time I made my first friend and he is still my friend.

MY PLACE IS
My place is the water around it.
My place is the bushes to go through to get to it.
My place is the fences to climb over.
My place is the long thick grass.
My place is the place only my friend and I know about.

EGG
I can only see the top of the egg.
It is like a dome with the sun shining off it.
If it was cooked it would look a lot different.

DREAM
It was a nightmare. It is a vague memory. I was confused. I found myself on the kitchen table. I remember running and jumping on a wall. I was probably sleep-walking.

FIRE
It makes me think of magic.
I smell the burnt matches.

It looks pink.
It amazes people.

Patricia Doherty

MY FIRST MEMORY
I remember when I met my first friend in Australia, and we went to the swimming pool and stayed as long as we wanted. We went to pre-school together and we lived across the road from each other. I remember when we used to play on the street and have races on our bikes.

I AM
I am the death of my cousin.
I am the day I made my First Confession.
I am the birth of my little cousin.
I am the first day of school.
I am the day we moved to Ireland.

PINK
Pink tastes very sweet.
Pink sounds like a baby crying.
Pink feels soft.
Pink looks happy.
Pink smells like pot pourri.

TURF
It reminds me of the hardened soil in my plant pot at home.
It sounds like a dice rolling along the table.

MY PLACE IS
My place is my bedroom where the private things that belong to me - nobody else knows where they are.
My place is the peacefulness when I sit at my window.
My place is the lovely view of the Swilly.
My place is the privacy I have when thinking about different things.
My place is the smell of my perfume that my sister uses.

MUSIC
It reminds me of films when people are thinking back.
It sounds like the singer had a child that wasn't well, and died.

AIR
Air is life and can be deaf.

Adrian Doherty

I AM
I am the day I made my First Communion.
I am the day I went to my godmother's wedding.
I am the day I started school.
I am the day I will make my Confirmation.
I am the day I started walking.
I am the day I started talking.

MY PLACE IS
My place is the garden where I can play football.
My place is the shed where I can play darts.
My place is my house.

THE BEST DAY
The best day of my life was when I got on our school football team.
A message came around to tell us whoever wants to be on the school team to
be in the PE hall at 3pm. I was one of the people who got picked and I was
very happy to be picked for the team.

FIRST THINGS
When I got up I smelled my breakfast.
When I looked out my window to see what kind of day it was, I saw the
sun shining in a blue sky.
I felt happy because I like good days.
I tasted toast and a cup of hot tea.
When I came to school I was sad and tired.

EGG
The egg looks like the hot yellow sun.
It smells like my mummy baking buns.
It feels sticky and wet.
It sounds like someone tapping on a table.

EARTH
It feels soft and cold.
It smells like wet moss.
It looks like sheep droppings.

It sounds like someone is using oil pastels when you rub it on your page.
I have seen it in my garden.
FIRE
The flame is making the candle smaller.
It is a bright orange.
It gives us light.
I can smell burning wax.
AIR
Air is empty.

Charlene McGowan

MY FIRST MEMORY
I remember when I was four, I was a flower-girl at my aunty's wedding. I wore a white dress and a blue ribbon around me. I remember everyone running about trying to get ready, while I was sitting ready to go to the hairdressers. I remember walking up the aisle and the bridesmaids walking behind me. The Mass was going on and on. I also remember my aunty gave me a chain to wear but I forgot it.

MY WORST DAY
My worst day was when my granny died. I loved spending time with her. I miss her but I always think of her in my prayers. I was sad when the coffin left the house. Tears trickled down my cheeks because I knew that the person I loved dearly is gone.
BLACK
Black looks like a black cat walking along the road.
Black tastes sour.
MISSING
Lost now forever
Hidden away in the dark
Please let him come back.
STONE
It looks like a piece of the moon.

MUSIC
It reminds me of the dead in my family.
It sounds like the people in it are sad.
It makes me feel sad like the day I heard about the Omagh bomb.
It looks like blue because blue is for sadness.

84

DREAM

I dreamed about a ghost following me all over the place. I could hear it breathing. I was all alone, and I was frightened. I tried to run away from it but it always followed me. I locked myself in my bedroom but I could still hear it breathing. Suddenly a knife rose in the air. I screamed with fright and woke up in my room crying.

EARTH

It reminds me of the graves of my grandparents which are covered in turf mould.

Joseph Berryman

BLACK

Black looks like coal.
Black smells like soot.
Black feels like water.

AIR

Air tastes like snow.
Air sounds like a breeze.
Air smells like lemonade.

TURF

It looks like tobacco.
It feels like worms.

MUSIC

It is a sad and peaceful song.
It is about a mother and a child.
It is a strange song.

DREAM

It was very strange. It was about Owen Doherty. He jumped into the Crana River.

Barry McLaughlin

BLUE

Blue smells like the breeze.
Blue tastes like water.
It is a cold colour.

MY PLACE IS

My place is my house.
My place is warm and cosy.

My place is where the sun shines in the window.
My place is a peaceful place.
My place is near my garden.

AIR
Air sounds like a whistling noise
Air looks invisible
Air is nothing

EARTH
The earth is a sphere.
It is one of nine planets.
The earth is our home.

FIRE
It reminds me of a dragon.
It is a small sea of orange and yellow.
People have relied on fire as a light, for years.
It will last forever.
It is silent and still.

FIRST THINGS
I got up, I saw the blue sky outside.
I felt cold in the kitchen.
I smelled toast in the grill.
I was very tired when I got up.
When I came to school I heard people talking.

STONE
It looks like a small meteorite.

Amy McCarter

MY FIRST MEMORY
My very first memory is when my grandfather died in 1992. I wasn't very sad because I was young and I didn't know what dying meant. I went up the stairs and into the bedroom and everybody was sitting around talking. I didn't know what was happening. My mother told me to say a prayer. So I went over to the coffin and said one.

GREEN
Green tastes like bitter lime.
Green feels like bumpy lettuce.
Green looks summery.

HAY
When someone mentions it, I think of horses.

MY BEST DAY

The best day of my life is the day I went to Disneyland and it was brilliant. There were lots of different rides like Splashmountain, Spacemountain, Ghosttown train - I can't even remember. My brother had a broken leg, so we skipped the queues. My brother wanted to meet Mickey Mouse. We spent the whole day there, and when we got back into our apartment, we weren't a bit tired.

MY PLACE IS

My place is my granny's house.
My place is the way the house is small and comfortable.
My place is the way the cooker gives out heat.
My place is the way the piano plays lovely tunes.
My place is the way I feel safe there.

FIRST THINGS

I felt the spring was definitely here.
It reminded me of somewhere I had never been before.
I saw the sunlight peering in the window of the classroom.

MUSIC

It reminds me of a funeral of one of my relatives. It was a very sad funeral. I was crying the whole way through it. She was very close to me. She was my aunt. Just seeing the coffin there in front of me, it would make anybody cry. At least she's still with me in my prayers.

DREAM

I can't remember when I had this nightmare but I was very scared. It happened in my house. Everybody had gone away, then my mum came back and told me everybody had died in a car crash and I ran off crying. Then I realised I had woken up, and I was crying in my bed.

AIR

It sounds like someone shaking out a bed cover.
Air is the substance we live on.

FIRE

It is the light of God.
It means to me a flicker of hope.
It changes as I gaze into it for ages.
It has two very different magical colours.
It guides the way out of the darkness.

Laura Doherty

MY FIRST MEMORY

I remember when my granda was alive. We used to run down the hall and drink the Holy water. He would come out and chase us. Then he would pick us up and take us to school in his little blue car. I remember the first day he took me to play school. He took me in and played with me, then he went and bought me sweets and the teacher wouldn't let me eat them. I cried. I never went back again.

I AM

I am the day of my First Communion.
I am the day my granda died.
I am the day my great granny died.
I am the day that we went on holidays.
I am the day my aunt got married.
I am the first day I went to school.

MY PLACE IS

My place is the way the sun shines in through my bedroom window.
My place is the way I see everything out of my window.
My place is the way I curl up and go to bed and sleep.
My place is the way I can get peace and quiet.
My place is the way I keep everything secret.

TURF

It smells like the smell of my granny's open fire.
It looks like the bog at my uncle's.

MY BEST DAY

My best day is the day I went to Dublin to meet the President. I remember getting into the car. I got sick on the way. It was very exciting. We had a party in the garden in a big tent like a circus tent. There was music and food. After we had the party we got a tour of the house. A brilliant day. On the way back, we went shopping.

HAY

It feels like a grass when it's had too much sun.
It smells like my uncle's barn.

EGG

It looks like the sun reflecting in the still crystal water.
It smells like the chicken house in my uncle's.
It tastes like the yolk running down my plate.

DREAM

When I was eleven I had a dream about my friend Elaine. We were out for a walk and Elaine's sister was there, and she's three. Karen was holding my hand and then she let go and ran and ran. Elaine and I tried to catch her, but she ran onto the road and got knocked down. It was terrible just standing there and I woke up crying.

FIRE

Fire is heat.
Fire smells choking.
Fire puts you in a stare.
Fire is life.

WATER

It looks green with my coat reflecting on it.
It smells like the beach.
It sounds like my baby cousin splashing in the bath.

Peter Gallagher

MY PLACE IS

My place is the house where I eat and sleep.
My place is the house where I play.
My place is the house where my family lives.
My place is the house where I stay.

TURF

It is the fuel you put in the fire.
It comes in broken pieces.
It smells like the mud on your football boots.
It looks like something I shouldn't say.
It comes from the bog.

AIR

We would die without it.
The wind lives in it.
It is everywhere except space.
It has always been here.
It will be around us forever.
It is not visible.

MY BEST DAY, MY WORST DAY

The best day of my life was when I met Bill Clinton and Tony Blair and President McAleese.

The worst day of my life was when the Omagh bomb happened. I lost two of my friends. It was very sad going to their wake.

EGG
It is unpleasant to look at.
It could have been a chick.

FIRST THINGS
I woke up and smelled fresh bread for my breakfast.
I saw the steam of the kettle rising.
I felt very tired.
I went outside and played football.
Came inside again and felt fresh.
Heard the birds singing.

TEA
It looks like burned ashes or burned paper.
It smells like an out-of-date lemon.
It probably came from India.
It's lovely in a cup.

FIRE
Fire is an eternal light.
It has been around for centuries.
It flickers and then dies.
It singes.
It fights for life.
I could watch it forever.

Michelle McLaughlin

MY FIRST MEMORY
I remember when I was young, my grandad Bernard used to sing a song about me. It went something like this: *Wee Michelle went upstairs to ring the bell. She banged her head and fell back down again.* I don't really remember how it went. That is how I think it went. Every time we were in his house, when he was away, he would always bring back ice-pops, even if he didn't know. When I was five, he died. I remember not knowing what was going on. I was very sad.

I AM
I am the time I made my Communion.
I am the time I got a cat called Cookie.

I am the time my sister was born.
I am the night I went to Cyprus.
I am the first time I went to Birmingham with the band without my parents.

GREEN
Sounds like a grass-hopper.

MY PLACE IS
My place is the way the sun reflects off the water.
My place is the way the sand sticks to my feet when I am wet.
My place is the way the huge wave crashes against the rocks.
My place is the feeling I get when I jump off the diving board and hit the water.

MY WORST DAY
The worst day I ever had that I remember is when my granny took a heart attack and was rushed to hospital. It happened about two weeks ago. The phone kept ringing and every time it rang, I jumped. I thought it might be bad news. I could barely sleep that night. My mum was in hospital with my gran for the next couple of days. I was up visiting her and she is now out of hospital. My aunty looks after her. My other aunt is coming home today from England to stay for two weeks to look after her.

EGG
It reminds me of a daffodil because of its colour.
It reminds me of one time I was in my great uncle's house. He had chickens.
He gave me one of the chicken's eggs, and I dropped it and it went everywhere.
It smells like my granny baking.

STONE
It tastes like a hard boiled sweet.
It sounds like someone knocking on a door.
It's the colour of an old person's hair.

Yvonne Doherty

MY FIRST MEMORY
I remember the first time I got my own pet. It was a bird. I got it for Christmas. My sister woke me up, but she had seen the bird before me.
I called the bird Lucky. It was very small but now it is bigger.

I AM
I am the day I made my first Holy Communion.
I am the time my grannies died.
I am the time I got my dog.

GREEN
Green tastes of something sour and bitter.

MY PLACE IS
My place is the river running by.
My place is the trees swooping down.
My place is the sound of the water splashing up on the rocks.

MY BEST DAY
My best day was when my Dad came home from Denmark. He was gone
for seven weeks. We had to go down to the town to collect him at night.
We were all glad to see him. He brought all of us presents home.

My best day was when I was in Cadbury's World in England. We saw how
they made all the chocolate. They had made a chocolate model of
Coronation Street, because they sponsor it. We ate lots of chocolate.

MISSING HAIKU
Along the dark road
Came a car up behind me
I missed you, said Mum.

EGG
It sounds of cracking when the shell opens.
It reminds me of my Mum cooking.

MUSIC
It reminds me of a funeral because it's a sad song.
It reminds me of a song my Mummy sings.

WATER
Without water we would die.
It reminds me of the running waterfall near my house.
Snow falls and turns into water.

FIRE
Fire makes me think about a Sunday, when I used to go to my grandad's house.

Christine Gill

HAY
It smells like horses.

FIRST THINGS
I went downstairs to the kitchen.
I had tea and toast.
The tea was a creamy colour.
The toast had butter on it.
Mummy took my clothes out of the tumble-dryer.
They were lovely and warm.
I saw my black and white cat before I went to school.

EARTH
The earth is so dark.

FIRE
It is a creamy orange red.
If people touch fire they would burn themselves.
You can make paper old by burning the edges of it.
Sometimes the fire sparkles.
When you're sick you can sit beside the fire.
It's the light that brightens a dark room.

WATER
It reminds me of sweat on someone's forehead.
Water comes from wells.

MUSIC
I think it is a love song.
It's a girl that is singing.
She sings over and over again.
It is sad.
It reminds me of Celine Dion.

TEA
It looks like sea-weed.
It tastes like tea.
It feels like coffee grounds.

TURF
Reminds me of when I am lighting the fire.
It's dirty as coal.
It sounds like stones dropping.

Patrick Fletcher

MY FIRST MEMORY

My first memory is falling down the steps out my back. I got a big bruise on my head. I got my foot stuck on the pedal of my tractor and the tractor tipped and I fell down the steps.

I AM

I am the football club which is my favourite place.
I am the day of my First Communion.
I am the day my uncle died.
I am the day my cousin got married.
I am the day I went to school.

MY BEST DAY, MY WORST DAY

My best day was when I went to my cousin's wedding.
My worst day was when my uncle died. He took a heart attack and my dad went up to the hospital. He came down at eight o'clock and said my uncle had died. It was very sad. That was my first worst day.

WHITE

Feels like snow and smells like sugar.

HAY

It smells like granda's barn.

FIRST THINGS

It smelled like a new day starting.
I heard the birds singing.
It felt like a summer's day.
It tastes like a hot drink of tea.

EGG

It looks like a bad sticky future.
It looks like the sun with a watery ring around it.
It smells like a dog who hasn't been washed.
It sounds like someone doing tap dancing when you bang the shell off the table.

TEA-LEAVES

It looks like fishes' droppings.

MUSIC

It sounds like something sad has happened.

94

It reminds me of when my uncle died.

DREAM
That I fell off a building and was falling very fast and I wakened up.

Owen Doherty

MY FIRST MEMORY
I remember when I got a Collie dog as a pet. His name was Prince. My Dad and I used to walk him at about twelve thirty in the morning. He never wanted to go for a walk and when we came back, he didn't want to go in. He was really lively and big but we gave him to our grandad because his dog died, and it was from his dog. I still see him at my granda's in Carndonagh and he still recognises me and I take him for walks.

I AM
I am the day we played the Inishowen Final.
I am the day I made my first Holy Communion.
I am the day I scored my first goal.

EGG
Eggs come from hens.
The shell is oval-shaped.
It looks like a flying saucer.

TEA-LEAVES
It looks like tobacco or dulse.
It smells like burnt paper.

MUSIC
It is a sad song about a mother and her child who is unlucky and strange.
It is very emotional.

HAIKU
They thought it was flat.
Columbus showed them it's round -
Found America.

FIRE
The flame reminds me of a belly dancer.
The flame stretches at full reach like a ballet dancer on her toes.
It can be there, then disappear, and return with the flick of a match.

Aidan McGinley

MY FIRST MEMORY
I remember very far back when I was really young. I was in my Dad's arms and I remember him feeding me with a bottle of milk and then remember him carrying me down to bed.

I AM
I am the day my granny died.
I am the day I started school.
I am the walks we took my granda on.
I am the day my granda died.
I am the day I made my First Communion.
I am the day I first went to Old Trafford.

RED
Red looks like danger.
Red tastes like tender meat.

FIRST THINGS
I saw the birds flying past my window when I woke up.
I heard them singing to each other.
I smelled the smell of my dad cooking himself a fry.
I smelled the car fumes in the car park.
I heard the sound of children talking.

MUSIC
It sounds like it's in an empty room.
It tastes like melted chocolate.
It smells warm.
It reminds me of a windy walk.
It sounds like something you would play at a child's funeral.

EARTH
It smells like a garden after the rain.
It looks like mouse droppings.
It sounds like someone playing in a wet sand-pit.

THE EARTH
It is slowly being polluted.
God created it for us to live in.

FIRE

It flickers like a dying sun.
Inside the yellow flame there is a blue flame.
It smells like burning wax.
It looks like a mini bonfire.

WATER

We can swim in it.
We need it to live.
It bubbles and it sounds like it is singing.

AIR

Is empty and invisible.

Jason Doherty

I AM

I am the first time I met my friend.
I am the time I made my First Communion.
I am the summer holidays.
I am the time my brother got knocked down and the doctors thought he wasn't going to make it.

MY FIRST MEMORY

I remember when my uncle died. He was on my mother's side of the family. He was a good man. He died of a massive heart attack at six thirty pm. Once my mother heard the news she was very upset. She said that all of us had to go to his funeral. He died on the 20th October 1995. I remember it was on a Friday. We left from Belfast to Liverpool. I remember my ears were popping. We went to the funeral and it was very sad.

MY WORST DAY

My worst day is when I was very sad when I heard about the Omagh bombing. But I paid no attention until the next. Till I heard it was the three boys that died. It was very sad in Buncrana and it was extremely sad when their bodies were driven up to Knockalla. Everybody held candles. We made a guard of honour for them. It was a sad day.

FIRST THINGS

I smelled breakfast.
I heard my Mum calling me to wake up.
I felt the sun shine, it was like a fire in my room.

I tasted the fresh cold milk in my cereal.

EGG

It looks like orange spittle.
It reminds me of my Dad shouting.
I like scrambled eggs.

THE EARTH

The earth is our home.
The earth is not the smallest.
The earth is not the biggest.
The earth is a football.

FIRE

Sun is fire.
Fire makes me think about Hell.
We use fire to cook things.
Fire puts you in a stare.
It lights up our hearts.

WATER

We need water to live.
It smells empty.
It is the waterfall near my house.
It reminds me of rain.

Darren McGlynn

MY FIRST MEMORY

I remember when I first went to Jersey. We went to the funfair and that was the best. We stayed at a hotel that had a big swimming-pool. The diving board was good. A year before that my best aunty died. She was the nicest aunty I had. She bought burgers for us and rented videos for us. She died in an operation.

I AM

I am the Buncrana football team. I play for them.
I am the Buncrana bridge where we fish.
I am the rave band called Scooter.
I am the day I made my first confession. I was scared.
I am the time my aunty died. I was sad.

PURPLE

Sounds like a car.
Is wine.

Is a soft towel.
Is my warm bed.

AIR
It smells like dried-out flowers.
It tastes like a burnt sausage.
It looks like a picture of the light sea.
It looks like snow falling smoothly along the ground.

MY BEST DAY
My second best day was at the funfair. We were having great fun and I
heard a big bang. I looked up and saw fireworks.

BLUE
Blue is a drink of water after a football match.

MY PLACE IS
My place is the sea-weed crackling under my feet.
My place is the fish jumping.
My place is the water I swim in.
My place is the crab that can nip.

TEA-LEAVES
It looks like mouse's dirt and tobacco.
It smells like spice.

EARTH
It is clay from the top of the Earth.

FIRE
The flame is a very hot thing.
It is a gas.
It can hurt you and melt your skin.
It makes me think about scoring goals.
Sometimes it is a very hard thing to describe.
It releases smoke like your breath on a frosty morning.
If you look at it for too long you can see it in your eyes.
It has a stem that keeps it lit.

WATER
It looks like a magnifying glass.

Emma Morrow

MY FIRST MEMORY
I remember the first day I went to school. It was a rainy and very cold day and I was crying. Amanda and I were fighting over a chair, and we started pulling each other's hair. She got the chair. At break time I saw the sixth class children, and I thought I was tiny.

I AM
I am the day my granny died.
I am the day my first cat was run over.
I am the day my granda died.
I am the day I met my first friend.

HAY
It smells like stables.
It looks like the rays of the sun.

EGG
It reminds me of a Saturday morning.
It sounds like fire cracking when the shell opens.

MUSIC
It is a slow song, sung very clearly. It reminds me of my granny's funeral.

EARTH
It's a sphere.
The earth has blue green colours.

FIRE
It reminds me of a cold Sunday afternoon.
It reminds me of the candles at my granny's funeral.
It is the light which lights the dark room.

WATER
It reminds me of somebody sick, and the sweat running down their forehead.

Hana Bruce
BLUE
Blue smells like violets.

MY PLACE IS
My place is the garden full of snowdrops in Spring.
My place is the horses which are lovely to ride.

AIR
Sounds like birds singing in Spring.
Tastes like icing on the top of a cake.
Feels cold in the winter.

MY BEST DAY, MY WORST DAY
My best days are those when I ride horses.
And there are the happy days when I worked in a race-horse stable - taking the
race-horses to Bundoran and going horse-jumping.

My worst day is when it is raining outside and the power is off and there is
a storm brewing, and my two baby sisters are crying.

HAY
It looks like string.
I have seen it in the race-horse stable.
It smells like silage.

EGG
It smells like the Saturday morning breakfast.
It reminds me of hens.
It sounds like the crackling of an egg on the frying-pan.

MUSIC
It reminds me of my great uncle's funeral.

DREAM
I was very small when I heard a noise outside, and I thought someone was
going to break into my house. Finally I fell asleep and dreamt that someone
had broken into our house. The next day my mum said that it was a badger.

FIRE
Fire. If you are in the dark it lights the room.
Fire is the colour of peace.

WATER
Water looks like the cold, cold sea.
It makes your hands clean.
Water only smells when you put it in tea or coffee.

Amanda McClintock

TURF
It looks like a burnt piece of wood.
It sounds like horses walking when you hit it off the table.

MY BEST DAY, MY WORST DAY
The best day of my life was when I was born. I think I brought happiness.
The best day was when I got my first pet. It was a budgie. I could talk to
him and he could talk back. He was very angry.

AIR
It sounds like a soft whistle from the wind.

RED
Red is supposed to mean danger.
It makes you feel warm.
Red is the colour of your heart.

MY PLACE IS
My place is the view from my house.
My place is the way the sun shines down on the water.
My place is watching the sheep eating grass.
When I was walking home
I found a dog dying.
I took it to the vet's.

HAY
It looks like strands of hair.
I've seen it in my rabbit's hutch.

MUSIC
It sounds sad.
It has got soft words.
It reminds me of my great granny's funeral.

EARTH
The earth is our home.

WATER
It reminds me of the swimming-pool.
You can see through it.

FIRE
It keeps us warm at night.

Fire is our enemy.
Fire gives us light.
It reminds me of when we go camping.
It looks as if it is climbing for freedom.

Niall Barton

MY WORST DAY, MY BEST DAY
My worst day was when my granny and granda died.
My worst day was when I broke my arm.
My worst day was when Ireland lost the rugby.

AIR
It feels like a soft gust of wind.
It looks like a clear glass bottle.

YELLOW
Yellow feels like the sun's rays.
Yellow tastes like mustard.
Yellow smells like pollen.
Yellow sounds like a burning fire.

MY PLACE IS
My place is the dog's grave.
My place is the way to my apple tree.
My place is the way to where I keep my savings.
My place is the way to my bedroom.
My place is the way to the TV.
My place is the way to my friend's house.

MY FIRST MEMORY
I can remember when I was three-and-a-half and I came out from surgery from a hospital in Belfast. I had to get my kidney stones out, and the Fire Brigade came to see me, but I was not well enough yet, so they came a couple of days later. Then I had to go out to see them.

SUGAR CRYSTAL
It's sweet.
Under a magnifying glass it looks like crystal.

I AM

I am the first day I learnt to walk.
I am the first dogs we had. They were called Murphy and Sean.
I am my first bike. It was blue.

HAY

It tastes like rushes.
It looks like dried grass.
It sounds like a crisp packet rattling.

EGG

It looks like a deformed sun.
I didn't touch it.
It reminds me of a dead bird.

WATER

It looks like a magnifying glass.
It reminds me of the shower.
It reminds me of a puddle.

EARTH

It looks like a big blob.
It reminds me of football.

FIRE

Fire can be our friend.
It gives us light.
It reminds me of a yolk in an egg.
It looks as if it is climbing.

Jacqueline Dixon

RED

Tastes like salt and water.

MY PLACE

Is where my house is.
My place is the way the hills are.
My place is the view when you look out of a window.

AIR

Air - it looks like nothing.
Air - it is like the wind.
Air - it sounds very quiet.

MY BEST DAY, MY WORST DAY

My worst day was when I got sick.
My best day was when I was off school.
My worst day was when my granny died.
My best day was when my sister had a baby.
My best day was when I got a goldfish.

MY FIRST MEMORY

I remember the first time I started to walk. My sister was sitting on the floor. She had a sweet in her hand and she showed it to me. I walked to get the sweet. I fell in the middle of the floor.

I AM

I am the day my granny died.
I am the day I got my donkey.

EGG

It looks like a flying egg in the sky.

DREAM

I had a dream one night. It was about my family. We were going on holiday to see my aunt and on the way we crashed the car. Then I woke up.

FIRE

It is like a star twinkling in the sky at night.
It is like sitting inside of the sun.

WATER

It is a liquid.
It looks like the colour silver.

David McAuley

TURF

It reminds me of the hill.
It reminds me of my Dad putting them on the trailer.
It smells like fresh country air.
It feels like the side of the house wall.

AIR

You can hear it whistling.

MY WORST DAY
My worst day was when I woke up one morning and spilt my breakfast.
The door whacked me on the side of the face.

RED
It's always there, wherever you look.
It smells like danger.
The word sounds like bed.

MY PLACE IS
My place is the way that there's water.
My place is where there is a hedge.
My place is the secret spy-hole.
My place is the way it protects me.
My place is where the sun gleams through.
My place is where no-one knows.

MY FIRST MEMORY
My first memory is when my mum woke me up and said *Your first day*. She had
the camera out taking pictures. And mum putting me into the car. The next thing
was teacher and walking into the classroom and seeing all those people.

I AM
I am the importance of my cat Multi and my dog.
I am the importance of my mum and dad.

EGG
It looks like the top of an orange in the sea.
It has a shell to protect it.

MUSIC
It is sad song and it is trying to make you think the same.

DREAM
I have a dream one night and it was at school and someone burst into the school
and started shooting with a gun. Everyone ran out, but my foot got stuck!

FIRE
Looks like a peach.
It burns in my eyes.

WATER
It is a form of liquid.

When you look at it closely you can see though it.
You need it when you are hot.

Joanne Gamble

FIRE

It is small at first.
It flickers in the night.
It stands up like a god.
It comes from under the earth.
If you stare at it you could die.

EARTH

The earth has famine.
The earth has all kinds of animals.
The earth is a very small place.

DREAM

I was five years old. I was in my room and 1000s of sparks were coming in
and no-one could help me.

I was four years old and I was a Princess up on a horse and cart.

EGG

Eggs come from birds, especially hens.
If a bee is flying out of it, something bad is going to happen.
The yolk is brown, your heart is brown.

HAY

It looks like green pasta.
I feed it to my calf.

I AM

I am visiting my aunty in Cork.
I am visiting the zoo which is great fun.
I am visiting my aunt. She always gives us sweets.

MY FIRST MEMORY

My dog Star was hit by a car six years back and my mummy put him in my
house, and next day Star was gone. Mummy said that God has him.

AIR

It looks afraid.
It feels all love.

107

MY PLACE IS
My place is the soap Granny gave me.
My place is the cat she has.
My place is the room she sits in.
My place is the way she lives.

RED
Red feels like red hot lava.

MY WORST DAY, MY BEST DAY
My worst day was when my pet called Star died. I told you about him last week.
My best day was when we got Trixie. She was so cute. She has four sorts
of puppies.

Catherine Sweetman

MY FIRST MEMORY
I remember when we started play school. We had biscuits and a drink at
lunch, and some days we would go outside. We would play with toys and
I would always take the blocks.

SHELL
It looks like a tortoise shell.
It is like the shape of a hat you would wear in Spain.

MY PLACE IS
Is the aeroplane going into the cloud and coming back out.
My place is sitting far from the TV so the sun doesn't reflect on it.
My place is the sky going red in the evening.
My place is the excitement of Christmas Eve.

PURPLE
Purple smells like blackberries cooking.
Purple tastes like sugar.

GREEN
Reminds me of having a picnic in the green grass in the summer.

DREAM
I had a dream that my friends Bria and Deborah and I went to meet B*witched
at a concert and we got lost. And when we got home there was two of everybody, and we didn't know which one was real, and it was really weird.

I was walking to my friend's house and I saw a drunk man. He started calling then he began to chase me and I woke up.

I had a dream that my family went on holidays without me. I went to my friend's house and her mum rang them.

FIRE
I love to watch the flames get higher and higher,
Watching the wax running down.
It reminds me of a Bar-B-Q in the summer.

Faye Masterson

MY FIRST MEMORY
I remember falling down at the swimming pool and the blood was pouring onto my white socks. It was stingy and sore. Afterwards Mrs. Houston put some cream and a plaster on it.

SHELL
It sounds like the ocean.
It smells like fish.
It looks like a rocky mountain.

MY PLACE IS
My special place is our back garden.
My place are the bushes which cover it and you can go there if you want some peace and quiet.
My place has a big open space.
My place is a brilliant hide-out if you're playing hide and seek.

PERSON IN A NUTSHELL
My granny is very kind. She is very good to me, but sometimes she can be cross. Most times she is happy.

YELLOW
Tastes like a banana.
Yellow smells like a bitter lemon.

WOOL
It smells like baby powder.
It feels like my granny's cardigan.

FIRST THINGS

I saw the blinding yellow sun when I pulled my curtains back.
I smelled my breakfast.
I breathed the fresh air.
I passed my granny's house.

WHITE

Looks like an egg shell.
Smells like a new sheet.

FIRE

It is doing a dance on the candle.
It will burn you if you touch it.
It reminds me of when our lights went out.
Fire spreads quickly.

HERE COMES THE SUN

Sun gives us light in the morning.
It goes down in the evening.
Sometimes it will not come out.
It comes when we are in a car.
We get very hot, and then it goes away behind the clouds.
In the evening it sets until tomorrow.

Colleen Quigley

MY FIRST MEMORY

My first memory is the first time at school. I remember when I went in, I
thought it was great, but when my mammy went out of the school I started
screaming.

SHELL

It reminds me of a mountain.

MY PLACE IS

My place is my granny's house.
The special thing about it is that it is very cosy.

AIR

Air is invisible.
It reminds me of a ghost.
We can't see it.

I AM

I am the special thing - my family.

I am the first time I took Communion.
I am the dog that I have.
I am the day my granny's house was built.

PERSON IN A NUTSHELL
My very important people are my mammy and daddy. If I didn't have
them I wouldn't be alive. My mammy and daddy give me food and drink.
I love my mammy and daddy.

RED
Red tastes like paint.
It looks like the sun.

FIRST THINGS
I smelled the toast toasting in the toaster.
I saw the sun blazing in my face.
I tugged my hair as I brushed it.

POSTCARD
I am a palm tree on the beach. There are leaves on the top of me. When it
is windy it is very hard to stay up. When it is sunny it is very hot, and
sometimes I can't stick it.

DREAM
In my dream I was a little girl and my mummy and daddy and I were in
the car and somebody threw a bomb at the car and then I woke up.

FIRE
It reminds me of sitting on the couch near the fire and going to sleep.

Kilgar Porter

MY FIRST MEMORY
The first thing I can remember is sitting in the kitchen drinking a full bottle
of Pepsi with my dog beside me, and playing with knives and forks - with
Cahal in his garden.

SHELL
It looks like it's ready to break.

MY PLACE IS
My place is my room with the TV in front of me.
My place is the way I see my sister asleep at night.
My place is the long drive up to Coleraine to see my granny.

My place is the sun hitting you when you get off a plane in a hot country.
My place is the way you come into the sitting room on Christmas morning.

AIR
There is no way you can see it.
You cannot touch it either.
You can smell it only when something that has a smell is mixing through it.
It can get toxic if chemicals are mixed through it.

I AM
I am the day we got a new house.
I am the day I got my first bike.
I am the day my sister said her first word.
I am the day I got my room done up.

ANIMAL HAIKU
Our dog died last year
He bit my little sister
So he was put down.

PERSON IN A NUTSHELL
I like my little sister so much, because every time I get punished, she is
my friend. She has long brown hair and green eyes. I would not give her
up for anything in the world.
RED
When people get cut, I come out.
I can be dark or bright.

DREAM
I was about to knock on my front door when I heard my sister scream. I
ran to find her but she was lost. There was a search party the next day and
they found her dead. For the rest of my life I was very sad. Then I woke up.
It was just a dream.
FIRE
The flame has a yellow glow in the middle.
Coal can make a fire bigger than it already is.

Mairead Gill

MY FIRST MEMORY
I remember when I was about six I was over in my grandad's house and I

was on my sister's old bike. I walked the bike up the brae to the top. I turned the bike and went flying down the brae. When I was half way down, something happened. I remember going head first over the handle-bars, falling on the ground and hurting my chin. I have a scar under my chin now.

SHELL
I think if you were in a bad mood you would hold this very tight till it would break.

MY PLACE IS
My place is across the road, where there were lots of trees.
There was a terrible storm which blew down some trees, and some of them crashed into my special tree.

AIR
The air sounds like a humming noise.

I AM
I am the day I had Christmas dinner with my family in our new house.

PERSON IN A NUTSHELL
My best friend is Mary Flanagan. We have been friends for three years and have never had any serious fights in our time. My mummy and daddy are very important to me. My mammy has brown hair and my daddy has grey black hair. My mammy has a big family but two of her sisters died at birth. My daddy comes from a big family as well, but his brother died. I don't know what I would do without my parents.

WINTER HAIKU
Snow comes in winter
My birthday is in winter
We play in the snow.

PURPLE
It tastes like a grape.

POSTCARD
I am wearing a pink dress and a gold necklace and bracelet. The weather is very warm. I am doing this job to feed my children and myself.

HAY
It feels like your fingers running through someone's hair.
It smells like a brandy ball.

FIRST THINGS

When I woke up this morning I could hear my alarm clock going off and I heard my special cousin crying.
I saw my mum sitting in the kitchen eating her breakfast.
I tasted my chocolate cereal this morning.

Deborah Kelly

MY FIRST MEMORY

I remember starting school. I could see all the boys and girls. I burst into tears when my mother was going and then the teacher came over and said it was all right.

SHELL

It smells like it's been under the deep sand for a long time.
It sounds like the wind blowing hard.

MY PLACE IS

My place is my granny's house.
My place is the beautiful view of the beach - the noise you can hear of her bird chirping.
My place is the noise of the sea and the noise of cars going up and down the road.
My place is the smell of my granny's fire burning.

AIR

Air smells like wild flowers.
It feels like putting your hand on a fluffy white cloud.
It sounds like the wind whistling and howling.

I AM

I am the day I received Holy Communion.
I am the day of my birth.
I am the day I got a baby sister.
I am the day I first went to my friend's house.
I am the day I got a pram and doll.

PURPLE

Purple feels wild and dry.
Purple feels like squashing a piece of material.
Purple rainbow stripe.

WOOL
It feels like running your hands through a dog's tangled hair.

POSTCARD
I'm out in the market today trying to earn my fortune. I have been working here since I was twelve years old. I sit in the sun all day, because I have to earn money for my family, to keep us from sleeping on the streets.

BLUE
Is a calm, cool colour.

FIRE
I like to watch the fire as the smoke rises up and you can see the blur of the smoke.
The smell reminds me of cooking marshmallow beside a bonfire on Halloween night.

Christopher Hegarty

MY PLACE IS
My place is the old house across the road.
My place is the corner beside my house where all the cars crash.
My place is the old cow behind my house, which has been there as far as I can remember.

MY FIRST MEMORY
I remember my first year at school. When I came in I saw some children crying, and a wee house down the back of the room. My teacher looked scary. Also kind.

AIR
Inside the air is hot and stuffy.
Outside the air is cold, fresh and damp.
Air is dusty in an old, creepy house.
Air is cold in a place like Buncrana.

I AM
I am the day of my birthday.
I am the summer holidays that come in July.
I am the dinner at Christmas.
I am the Buncrana Festival.
I am the cinema where I watch movies.

WINTER HAIKU

I will go to play
To play outside in the snow
Iced ponds everywhere.

RED

Red tastes like blood.
Red looks gloomy.
Red feels soft and round.

WOOL

It smells like my gran's house.
It reminds me of dog's hair.

FIRST THINGS

I woke up exhausted.
I felt delighted that the morning was not as cold.
I felt the warm, stuffy air turn fresh as I walked out of the door.
I saw the sheep grazing in the gleaming wet grass.

WHITE

Reminds me of rivers with a foamy cover.
Feels spongy, and my hand will go straight through.

DREAM

I was running through the fields with a bull after me. It had big horns and
was running very fast. Muck was skiting everywhere. The field was wet
and soggy. My feet felt like a million tonnes, and he was right behind me.
When I came to the wall, then I woke up sweating and screaming.

FIRE

It glows with its own hot burny flame.
It smells like burnt paper.
It is dangerous in its own way, but it is also very helpful.

Nicola McLaughlin

MY FIRST MEMORY

My earliest memory is sitting in a pram with the rain cover over me, and
my grandmother pushing me through Swan Park to see the horse Barkley.

MY PLACE IS

My place is the playground in school. I can be there with all of my friends.

116

My place is the graveyard. I can sit at my uncle's and granda's grave and tell them how much I love and miss them.
My place is the director's chair in my room. I can imagine myself directing a Hollywood movie.
My place is the house my grandma lives in.
My place is the house I live in.

SHELL
I imagine it would taste like salt water.
It reminds me of being at the beach and playing in sand.
It looks like a torn sombrero from Mexico.

PORRIDGE
It looks like rabbit food.

AIR
When you breathe in through your nose, air leaves a tingly feeling.
It feels like pins in your face if its cold.
Strong winds remind me of a big man roaring.
Air blowing reminds me of being in a warm kitchen with the fan going full blast.

RED
Feels furry.

I AM
I am the first time my tooth fell out. I got money under my pillow.
I am the dog I used to have. His name was Spencer, but on 17th May he ran away. He was furry and brown and one in a million.
I am the mouse I had who was called Alvin, but he died shortly after an operation.
I am the necklace my grandmother gave me. She made it when she was fifteen. It has pink jewels and diamonds and is really beautiful.

PERSON IN A NUTSHELL
My grandma Doherty is kind and loving. She doesn't refuse me anything. She has blonde curly hair and she is brilliant.

FIRST THINGS
When I drew my curtains this morning, my whole room filled with an amazing brightness.
As I walked to school this morning, I felt the understanding between my friend and myself.
When I was in the playground I felt happy and accepted.

BLUE
When I see the colour blue I go into a trance and think about the sea and the fish swimming through it, or sometimes think about the bird flying through the deep blue sky.

DREAM
A dream that really sticks out in my mind is one where I was lying in my bed and a ghost appears in front of me. I recognise the face, but don't know who it is. It seems to swallow me, and I can't see anything. Then I was in my mother's bedroom and saw my dog Spencer lying dead on the ground. It seemed as though I was inside a hurricane, spinning round and round, with all my greatest fears spinning round beside me. I started to scream and woke up feeling dizzy and sick.

FIRE
Fire is the light that never dies away.
Fire is the stars on a moonlit night.
Fire is a godsend, it's every person's light.
Fire can be dangerous, can cause the loss of life.
It reminds me of a chapel, and Jesus on the cross.

Bria Murphy

MY PLACE IS
My place is the poky hole upstairs in my house.
My place is the inflatable chair in my bedroom.
My place is the bed in my Nana's house, where I sleep when I stay.
My place is the chair where I sit in the class.
My place is the summer seat in my aunt's house in Holland - the balcony that looks over a cyclist bridge.

SHELL
It sounds like a radio gone all fuzzy.
It feels like ridges of stone.
It reminds me of a periwinkle.

I AM
I am the day that I get my brace, which is soon. It will make my teeth straight.
I am the day that I passed my piano exam because I was relieved.
I am the watch on my arm because I am forgetful.
I am the parents I have.

PORRIDGE OATS
It tastes like yeast.
It looks like bird food.
It reminds me of my Nana's.

RED
Red is like anger.
Red smells like smoke.

PERSON IN A NUTSHELL
My mammy and daddy are important to me because they look after me and protect me. They are proud of me. My mammy is tall and has brown hair. My daddy is also tall and has brown hair. My mammy comes from a big family and she works as a garment technician in the Fruit of the Loom. My daddy comes from a big family also and works as an interior designer. My parents are wonderful.

FIRST THINGS
I have tasted powdery chocolate spread on my sandwiches.
I have smelt the grass of Spring when I first went outside.
I have seen all the children in my class lined up at break-time.
I have felt the slippery covering on my pen when I started to write.

INDIGO
Indigo is the deep deep purple you can only find in flowers.
It is the smell that comes out in Summertime.

DREAM
When I was little I used to sleep downstairs and I thought an orange man was running around my room upstairs. We were driving past my house and I could see him grinning. It was so bad I can still remember it clearly. Sometimes I get déjà-vu when I am dreaming and something from my dream comes true.
I used to think that one side of the bed was a bad side for nightmare and the other side was good.

FIRE
Fire smells like burnt charcoal.
Fire looks like a luminous orange.
Fire sounds like two stones rubbing together hard.
Fire feels like warmth against your hand.
Fire reminds me of a Chapel.

Séana McDaid

MY FIRST MEMORIES
My first memory is when I was in Scotland I can remember I had to go every day to a neighbour's house when I came home from school. I remember I went to a party of a person I hated and didn't tell my mum. I remember I had two goldfish, and I remember the day we left Scotland.

SHELL
The shell reminds me of the fish.
It sounds like the tide.
It looks like a small mountain with snow on top.

MY PLACE IS
My place is my granny's house. It is a special place.
My place is my granny. She is a special person.
My place is warm and cosy.
My place is the street which is always quiet and peaceful.

AIR
It has no shapes or sizes.
Air is everywhere.

I AM
I am the day I first took Holy Communion.
I am the day of my cousin's eighteenth birthday.
I am the day I got my two kittens.
I am the day I went to Scotland and met all my old friends.

PERSON IN A NUTSHELL
My granny is important to me. She cares for me when I am sick. Her kind-heartedness is the best thing about her. I love her very much.

BLUE
Blue tastes like salt water.

WOOL
It looks like knotted up thread.
It reminds me of my granny's cardigan.

FIRST THINGS
In the car coming to school, I smelt the smell of my sick cat, because we had been to the vet yesterday.

I saw the bright yellow sun from my window.

RED
Looks like sunburned skin.

FIRE
If you touch it you get a burn.
It looks as if it's doing a dance.

Joseph Flynn

MY FIRST MEMORY
My granda was at the house for his birthday and said to me *Come on, we'll go to the shop.* Then he said, *Stop jumping around on the couch,* and scolded me.

MY PLACE IS
My place is my granny's back garden.
My place is London because my granny and granda live there.
My place in Buncrana is Swan Park.

AIR
It keeps you cool when it is hot.
It feels like the feather of a bird.
It's there but you cannot see it.

I AM
I am the day we won the Inishowen League.
I am the day I got a brother.
I am the day I caught my first fish.
I am the day I made my first Communion.
I am the love I have for my mammy and daddy and family.

FIRST THINGS
I woke up this morning and my room was like a pig-sty.
I went out and saw all the bright light and colours.

POSTCARD
I am a pot. My name is Jack. It is very hot. I do it for the starving people. I do not like it. The flames are under me. They go straight into me. I am cooking food for the woman beside me and her child.

RED
Red is the colour of love.

FIRE
It is a bright light above the clouds.
It lights up rooms.
It reminds me of a house I went into. It had lots of candles.

Kerrie Ferguson

MY FIRST MEMORY
When I was young I remember my daddy had a light in the garage and there was a man on it and I was frightened.
And I remember when I had a black cat and a dog ate it.
I remember getting porridge for my breakfast and I went upstairs and mummy helped me to get dressed for school.
The first day I went to school my mummy tried to go without me, and I ran after her.

SHELL
It tastes like a piece of sea-weed.
It feels like a sharp blade.

MY PLACE IS
My place is a good secret place.
My place is the house my granny and granda lived in. It is in Fermanagh.
My granny just died on Sunday, 31st January. I'm glad my granny has died because she is not suffering any more but I am not glad that she is gone. I have a chain belonging to her. It has diamonds on it. My sister got a chain too.
My place in Buncrana is a place called Swan Park.
The thing I like most is my hamster and my granny's chain.

PORRIDGE OAT
It feels like a fine piece of cloth.
It reminds me of snow breaking up.

AIR
It can give you oxygen.
It can be polluted.
We can't see it.
If the air stops, we stop.

I AM

I am the chain that belonged to my gran who died.
I am the ring that was my aunty Barbie's. She died in 1996.
I am the love I have for my mummy and daddy.
I am the love I have for my hamster.

BLUE

It tastes like blue slush puppy.
It feels like paint.
It reminds me of the day I walked into a new house decorated in blue.

PERSON IN A NUTSHELL

My favourite person is my little baby cousin. His name is Conor McGlynn. If he cries I say to him, *Are you coming to see Po* (that is what they call their terrapin). If he doesn't stop crying, I would say *Come and see the digger.* When he comes out to my house he runs up my hall and into the room where my hamster is. I run after him.

WOOL

It smells like a carpet.
It reminds me of a glass of red wine.

FIRST THINGS

When I first woke up, I saw my brother. I lay awake in bed. It looked like the sun was splitting.

WHITE

It looks like a snowman.
It's the colour of winter.
It sounds like a crunching noise.

FIRE

It can cause a real blast.
It can cause lives to be lost.
But I like the warmth of the fire.
It could make you fall asleep.

John Duffy

MY FIRST MEMORY

I remember my first day at school. My aunty was the teacher.

SHELL
The shell smells like salmon that's off.

MY PLACE IS
My place is the colours at the end of the field behind my house.
My place is the birds that fly down onto the fence.
My place is the bird feeder they always peck at.
My place is the big pool of water on the field when the rain falls.

AIR
If you move your hand you can feel the air going through your fingers.
You can hear it hitting against the window.
You cannot smell it, but if you could, it would smell like a cold hand.

I AM
I am the time I got my first bike.
I am the time I made my first confession.
I am the time I had my eleventh birthday.
I am the time I went to my first pantomime.

ORANGE
Orange feels like a sphere.
Orange is coloury.

PERSON IN A NUTSHELL
He has blue eyes and black hair. He stays with you through thick and thin.
He lives in Gransha Road. He has a big room and he always gets something for his mum when he is up the town.

WOOL
It feels like a piece of fur from a bear.
It looks like a piece of rope.
It reminds me of a tangled-up dog.

FIRST THINGS
I woke up and felt the warmth of my small snug room.
I heard two gigantic knocks at our glass door.
I smelt the fumes of the engine. It was like a rotten egg being cracked.
I saw cars and little children and big children going to school.

DREAM
I dreamed that my dad had forgotten to put on the hand brake and I rolled the whole way down to the fence in the car.

FIRE

Fire looks like inside an egg.
Fire smells like a piece of coal.
It sounds like a person whistling.
If you tasted it it would taste charred.

BRIDGE

I go to the bridge
The one that is still standing.
The bridge that is old.

Bernadette Devlin

MY FIRST MEMORY

My memory is of when my granny died. It was very sad because every
day after school, I would go to my granny's house. Now I can't because
she's died.

SHELL

It looks like a very small hat.

MY PLACE IS

My place that I like is my brother's house.
My place is the ocean.
My place is my granny's grave.

PORRIDGE OAT

It feels lumpy.

I AM

I am the day I got my new bike.
I am the day I made my Holy Communion.
I am the dog I have had since I was six.
I am the day I went for a meal with my family.

PERSON IN A NUTSHELL

My mummy and daddy are important to me because they took care of me
when I was small and they are good to me now.

WOOL

It feels like rubbing hair together.

FIRST THINGS

This morning my mummy came into my room and drew the curtain and I
thought I was blind from the light.
I heard the sound of my daddy snoring.
When I set off for school I saw a beautiful bird.

GREEN

It tastes like lettuce and looks like my room.

DREAM

When I was about eight, I went to the pictures with my brother and sister to
see Jurassic Park. When we came home I went to bed and I had a nightmare
about dinosaurs all night.

FIRE

It keeps us warm.
It's a flame in the day and nothing at night.

Shaun Quirke

AIR

If you move your body through air, you will find a breeze going through
your fingers.
When you blow air through a small gap in your mouth, it's called a whistle.
If air comes through a door, this is called a draught, which can leave people
with a sore back.
It cools people down when there is a heat wave.

I AM

I am the day I was born.
I am the day I was baptised.
I am the day I made my First Communion.
I am the day I got my dog. It is cuddly and it is mine.
I am the day granda gave me his binoculars.

WOOL

It smells like dye.
It has a feeling like patting a dog.
It makes me think of a homeless person's hair.
It sounds like a bit of fluff from a pillow.

FIRST THINGS

I heard the sound of my little niece crying for a bottle.
I woke up and the sun was shining in my eyes.
I felt the draught of wind coming through the door as my sister left at half
past eight.
I got up and went to school and I was five minutes late.
I wait patiently for three o'clock for rounders.

BLUE

Rain is blue and dropping on the pane.

DREAM

I was flying over a farm with lambs and sheep. The trees were blowing
gently and the dog was jumping with joy and couldn't get settled because
the grass was blowing, and in the distance I could see the waves crashing
on the sand of Lough Swilly beach and the children were playing making
sand castles and swimming in the sea.

FIRE

Carbon monoxide can kill.
But if we didn't have fire we wouldn't be able to heat ourselves up
Or cook food like potatoes or vegetables.

HERE COMES THE SUN

The sun comes up in the morning
And leaves in the afternoon
And I tell you now
It's a lovely sight to see the sun going down.

Caolán Deery

DREAM

My worst nightmare was when I was on the edge of a cliff. Kyle pushed me
off. As I was going to fall, I pulled Kyle with me. We were falling for ages.
Before we hit the ground, I woke up.

MY FIRST MEMORY

I remember coming into school with my mum and sitting in a seat beside
John and playing with a jig-saw.

SHELL
It feels like a cone.
It looks like a hill.

MY PLACE IS
My place is Disneyland. There are a lot of roller coasters there and it is huge.
My place is San Francisco, where the Golden Gate bridge is. I like San
Francisco for its sunshine.

HAIKU
I have just got a dog.
I gave him a name, Lucky.
He's three months old.

PERSON IN A NUTSHELL
His name is Austin. He has blue eyes and brown hair and he's my godfa-
ther. I only saw a photograph. I only saw a video. Now he's gone.

BLUE
Tastes like water.
Blue smells like paint.
Blue looks like an ocean.

AIR
You cannot see it.
It smells like smoke.
It feels like a fan blowing in your face.

I AM
I am the day I bought my Play Station.
I am the day I first received Holy Communion.
I am the day I got my puppy, Lucky.
I am the day I got my cat Whiskers.

HAY
It looks like a string of real hair.
It feels like wool.
It reminds me of a pipe-cleaner.

FIRST THINGS
I smelled my breakfast my mother was making.
I passed the chapel on my way to school.
I saw birds flying past the school with food for their young.

POSTCARD
I am a tyre rolling around on the ground on a cart holding eight people. I might burst any second now with the weight. I get my face rolled in sand all the time. I travel through South India.

BLUE
It is the colour of my room and my bike.

FIRE
It gives out heat when we are cold.
It can burn places down sometimes.

HERE COMES THE SUN
The sun is coming out from behind the clouds.
The sun is shining bright and clear.
Everybody is out to play.
The sun has let us out today.

Lorna Caldwell

FIRE
Fire flickers in the breeze like a whisper going from ear to ear.

BRIDGE HAIKU
If you build a bridge
You can make a brand new friend
Best friends all your life.

DREAM
I had a dream about a house fire. Everyone was doing normal things and they started to rush outside. I followed them and when I was outside, I looked up onto the roof and it was ablaze. The Fire Brigade were already there. I was taken away and then I woke up.

WOOL
It looks like a piece of red hair.
It feels like stuffing inside teddies.

FIRST THINGS
It was dark when I woke up.
I smelled the exhausts of cars on my way to school.
I could feel the coldness on my fingertips.

I heard the sound of people jabbering and talking.
I could see the mountains on my way to school.

POSTCARD
I am a dog sitting lazily while my owners are working their hearts out. I am brown and white. There are women carrying baskets. I think one woman is cursing another. I think some people might be making tea.

RED
Red smells like bubble-gum.
It looks like blood.
It tastes like ketchup.

PERSON IN A NUTSHELL
She's sometimes cheeky. She is two years old. She bites and kicks. She loves wrestling. She loves Barney and the Morbegs. She always gets her own way, but she's special to me, my baby sister Gemma.

MY FIRST MEMORY
I was about four. I was looking into a shed full of hay, and seeing a tiny scared puppy which went and hid behind the bales of hay. I remember the smell of the freshness of the shed, and the little puppy's face.

SHELL
It looks like a miniature mountain.
It feels sort of rippled when you touch it.

Cahal Crossan

MY FIRST MEMORY
When I was two years old I got a dog called Ben, and when I was three, my little brother got christened. I can remember my third birthday when I split my head and jammed my finger in a car door. I can remember when I got my finger bitten by my friend's dog. I can remember jumping into the pool.

SHELL
It looks like a turtle shell.
It feels like a hollow stone.
It sounds like a knock on the door.

MY PLACE IS

My place that I love is the Inch riding stables, with my horse asleep. And once I fell asleep with his night rug over me, in the stable. But now he is in Swan Park. I like that place too, because I am with my horse.

My place is the grave of a young pony.

My place is the house of my uncle, because that is where my daddy recovered from a bad car accident.

AIR

I can smell Dettol in the air.

Hot air rises and cold air sinks.

I AM

I am the thing that is important to me. It is my daddy's Scalectrix set. The track is over thirty years old and if anyone broke it...

I am the thing that is important - my pony.

I am my family.

I am the dog.

PERSON IN A NUTSHELL

It would have to be my granny and my mammy and daddy. Because if my granny was not there for me, I would not have a proper family.

HAIKU

I have got a dog.

His name is Maximilian.

He's a spotted dog.

RED

I'm getting my gate painted red.

WOOL

It reminds me of plaiting my mummy's hair.

It is very tickly.

It is a winey colour.

FIRST THINGS

I saw houses and cars, people and birds - shops that were closed, shops that were open. I saw people with school bags and people with none.

FIRE

It reminds me of a fire that I put coal in.

The fire and hot coal came out and the carpet went on fire. I put it out.

Fire can cause death.

Fire can save lives.

HAIKU

I live near a bridge
It is made of stone and rock
I go everyday
I have a horse there
When he goes under the bridge
I have to get him.

Kyle Doherty

MY FIRST MEMORY

I remember in play school I bit Lee Stone's leg, because he was throwing
my picture under the table. My mum was helping that day.

SHELL

It looks like an old metal army hat.

MY PLACE

My place is beside the Mill River. I like to listen to the water.
My place is my bed, because it is comfortable.

PORRIDGE OAT

It sounds like bits of ice falling on wood.

AIR

You cannot see it.
It can be strong.
It can be a killer.

I AM

The day of my First Communion.
I am the Christmas that happens every year.
I am the day when I get my money.
I am the day when I got my dog.

RED

It tastes like tomatoes.
I hate tomatoes.
Red looks like a heart..

PERSON IN A NUTSHELL

My mum gave birth to me. My parents raised me from when I was born.

They feed me. I love them. I hope they love me.

WOOL
It feels like finely plaited hair.
It tastes like string.
It reminds me of a falling feather.

FIRST THINGS
I rose from my bed and reached for my clothes, but plummeted and dozed off.
As I went into the school, the smell of the waxed floor in the PE hall
smacked me on the face.
In class, the sight of books hit me.
I also saw the jungle-like plants on the window-ledge.
I was joyous to tell Kilgar he could sleep at my granny's.

FIRE
The flame surrounds the wick of the candle.

HERE COMES THE SUN
The sun rises above the hills in the morning.
Stays standing proud in the sky, lighting our way.
It stands for hours, gleaming.
The moon over-powers it and it hides behind the hills waiting for another day.

James Doherty

MY FIRST MEMORY
I remember the first time I was in Galway. I was two or three at the time
and we were staying at my mammy's friend's house. I was outside running
about on the tarmac beside the kerb, when I tripped and fell.

SHELL
There is a sort of stencil of a fish inside.
It is like a pyramid.

MY PLACE
My place is the field in front of our house where our hut is.
My place is the bed in my room.
My place is the roof of one of our sheds.
My place is the pile and heap of stones in the quarry.

OATS
It tastes like barley.
It smells like corn.
It reminds me of bird feed.

AIR
It keeps us alive.
It carries dust.
It makes the birds fly.

I AM
I am the time when I will get a car of my own.
I am the time when I got my new bike.
I am the first time I drove our forklift.
I am the time I made my first Holy Communion.
I am the dog of ours. It is important.

BLUE
Tastes like the ocean.
Blue feels like wet paint.
Blue looks like a bluebird.

HAIKU
I like engines much
They can take us anywhere
That we want to go.

PERSON IN A NUTSHELL
My mother and father. They have fed me from the day I was born, and my
father lets me drive a lot. My friend Stephen who is getting married in
June. He taught me to drive.

FIRST THINGS
I sighted the atmosphere of the classroom.
I smelled the new PE equipment.
I sighted the marble on the altar.
I heard the rushing of passing cars.

GREEN
Green is the colour of our environment.
It tastes like a pear.

FIRE
Fire makes me feel warm.
It is the thing we need most.
There is a bonfire night every year.

Rory Devlin

MY FIRST MEMORY

I remember far back, the first time I was on a motorbike. I was quite scared at first, because I was only six years of age. But when I was on the bike for a minute it was fine.

MY PLACE

My place is in England.
My place is called Brans Hatch.
My place is a motorbike circuit. The motorbike riders that race there are my favourites.

HAIKU

My dog's name is Rex
He ran away yesterday
He came back today.

RED

Tastes like ink.

WOOL

It looks like knitting wool.
It smells like dye.
It reminds me of my dog.

FIRST THINGS

First thing I saw this morning was my brother pulling the blankets off me and telling me to get up for school.
I saw light hitting my eye
And on the way to school I saw the sun beating down on me.

POSTCARD

I am a bull. I work for people pulling ploughs and I am complaining to other cows about it. It is very hard work. Sometimes I would like to run off into the woods. I do not like slaving for people. They are planting rice. I live in South India.

BLACK

Black reminds me of my bed at night.
It feels like a smooth black Porsche - all throb.

FIRE

It makes me think of fire blowing through the forest and people fire-fighting for their lives.

It looks like the sun beating down on a hot summer's day.
It reminds me of when my hand got burnt.

Shauna Cooper

PORRIDGE OATS
It feels powdery.
It tastes milky.
It sounds crunchy.

AIR
You can see it when it hits the leaves on a tree.
It feels against your skin.
It sounds cold when it is windy.

I AM
I am the first day I went fishing.
I am the first time I clerked Mass.
I am the day of my First Holy Communion.
I am the time I came third in the Northern Ireland Championships.

FIRST THINGS
I woke up this morning and saw the light shining in at my window.
I was walking to school and heard the birds chirping.
Coming into school I smelt disinfectant.
I went outside at break-time and felt the cold.

I AM
I am the long flower reeds.
I am cream, blue and orange.
I am soft and cold.
I am the plants which will be sold.
I am the joy someone will have when they receive me for a present.

GREEN
I am green.
People think I am an unlucky colour.

FIRE
The beautiful bright flame.
The smell of burning.
The sound of the striking of the match.

It reminds me of when my two friends died in August.

HERE COMES THE SUN
Hitting us like rays of light.
Pushing clouds away.
Withering plants.
Burning people's skin. Making it turn red.

Michael Caldwell

HAIKU
I will go golfing
I will drive the golf ball far
Up and down the course.

BEST PERSON IN A NUTSHELL
My granda was in the navy. He helped people that were dying in World
War II and he brought people home and he got a medal. I did not see him
because he died.

RED
It smells like clothes coming out of the washing-machine.

FIRE
It is like a tube of steam.
It smells like a red rose.
I like the smell of fire.
It reminds us of the dead sometimes.

HERE COMES THE SUN
The sun is coming.
Very slowly.
It comes out from under the clouds
And shines very hard
Burning our skin
Like a tomato.

BRIDGE HAIKU
I live near a bridge
The bridge I live near is big
I went under it.

Owen McLaughlin

FIRST MEMORY

I remember as far back as my fifth Christmas Eve. I was sitting in my bed
writing a letter to Santa. Then I left some milk and cookies on the table
and went to sleep.

BRIDGE

The place I go when I am sad is the wee bridge.
The time my cousins turned on me I felt sad.

PORRIDGE OATS

It feels like bits of corn.
It reminds me of a field I used to know.

AIR

You can see it when tornadoes come.
It makes me glad to be alive.

I AM

I am the Christmas I got my Play Station.
I am the day my aunty got married. I had a great time.
I am the day I got my dog, but he ran away.
I am the day I got my cat.
I am the first time I was in our new car.

GREEN

Green tastes like parsley.

BEST PERSON IN A NUTSHELL

My daddy and mammy are the people I'm talking about. They take care of
me. They've raised me. They give me presents on my birthday. They tuck
me in at night. They let me stay up late on Friday and Saturday. When I
wash the car they give me money.

WOOL

It looks like a hair ball.
It reminds me of sheep.

FIRST THINGS

The light blinded me when I got up this morning and I felt exhausted.
When I came into school I was late and I saw everybody staring at me.
I tasted my cheese sandwiches at 11 o'clock.

FIRE
When I lie in front of the fire-place it makes me feel tired.

HERE COMES THE SUN
Up in the sky
So yellow and bright
It'll go at about seven.
It'll say good-bye to the day.
Say good-bye to the day.

Kevin Doyle

I REMEMBER
I mind when my grandad died and I was seven. I was very sad. I remember I had to go the funeral and I looked around and I saw everybody was sad. I think it was the year after that when my great granny died and I was very sad then too.

SHELL
It looks like a stone that has been halved.
It tastes like sand.
I hear the sea.

MY PLACE
My place is in Fahan.
My place is at the other side of the sea.
My place is a heap of mountains.
My place is beside my cousin's house.

PORRIDGE OATS
It reminds me of breadcrumbs.

AIR
I don't smell anything because it is so clean.
It is all around the earth.
We will breath it until the day we die.

I AM
I am the day I made my first Holy Communion.
I am the day I first caught a fish.
I am the day I was born.
I am the day I came into school for the first time.

SPECIAL PEOPLE IN A NUTSHELL
The people most important to me is my mummy and daddy. They do more

for me than anyone. The other person important to me is my granny.

FIRE

Fire was used years ago. People had no electric light.
Fire smells like wax.
It is very smoky.
We should not mess with fire.

HERE COMES THE SUN

I'm glad it has come, because last year we had no sun. It was like winter. I hope it comes this year.

Gary Sweeney

I REMEMBER

I remember my first day at Scoil Íosagáin. You could smell lunch boxes and I was very afraid. Then I made a friend. His name is Lee Magee.

MY PLACE

My place is the sea.
You can fish in
The sea and
The sun shines
Down on it.
Birds are
Flying above
It too.

SHELL

It reminds me of peace and quiet in the bed.

BEST PEOPLE IN A NUTSHELL

My mummy and daddy. They are very special. I love them.

DREAM

I was going to my friend's house and I had a football and I kicked it up in the air and it went into a field. I went to get it and suddenly I saw something. I ran out of the field and I looked back and saw flashing. I threw a stone at it and the flash was gone. Then my mummy woke me up.

FIRE

Fire reminds me of when you camp, you make a fire.

When you light a candle you can smell the wax and see it drop.
It is very hot and you can burn yourself.

HERE COMES THE SUN

Shining above the hill
Shining on the clouds
Shining on me

Pamela O'Hagan

I REMEMBER

I remember my grandad and I out on the grass playing ball. I fell and hit
my head.

SHELL

It feels like sand paper.
It looks like a minister's hat.

MY PLACE

My place is in my granny's house, in the sitting-room. I think it is very
relaxing. When you sit in the chair you can hear the breeze outside blowing against the trees.

I AM

I am the day that I went to Germany.
I am the day I found a baby kitten.
I am the day of the summer holidays.
I am the time my aunt got a new baby.
I am the time my granny got out of the hospital.

DREAM

I dreamed that me and my friend were in a car. We were in the car for
hours and we could not get out.

FIRE

It reminds me of big orange spikes
And the fire that burns on the fire-place at home.

HERE COMES THE SUN

Here comes the sun all bright orange and yellow.
When its bright light shines on you it makes you hot and sticky
As if you were in the desert.
And in the evening, the sun goes away.

BRIDGE

An old wooden bridge
About to fall into the river
All woodworm and rust
Water moving fast
Faster than the bridge falling.

Matthew Deeney

I REMEMBER

I remember the first day that I got my cat called Ginger. I was only five,
and I was afraid of her at the start, but then I lost that fear and I really like
her from then on.

MY PLACE

My place is when I go to Scotland. My mum's relations all live there. I go
to one of my Mum's brothers and see my cousin Aubin. He is twelve years
old. They live in Perth. My other cousins live in Biggar. The thing I always
remember is the park in Biggar in front of my cousins' house.

OAT

It tastes like Holy Communion.

AIR

Sometimes you can see polluted air.

I AM

I am the day my nephew was born.
I am the teddy I have had since I was born.
I am the time we get off school.
I am the dog I had a few years ago.
I am the uncle I have in America.
I am the way I love my family.

BEST FRIENDS IN A NUTSHELL

I love my mother and father because they always take care of me, and
always let me do things and go places.

HAIKU

My name is Matthew
This poem is called haiku
It is very short.

WOOL
It looks like thread hanging from your jumper.
Or a piece of spaghetti.
It feels tickly.
It smells like dust.

FIRST THINGS
When I woke this morning the smell of my brother's feet was the first thing that hit me.
When I was coming into school, the sight of my friends playing football was the first thing I saw.
When I opened the door of the class I saw the Oliver Twist picture and that reminded me of our Christmas play.

FIRE
Fire is used in remembrance.
When someone dies you see candles lit beside the coffin.
Fire can also kill people in their own houses.
When you hear the expression 'It burns the throat off you,' if you tasted fire, that's what it would do.
It reminds me of when my friend died in Omagh. At his wake all the candles were lit around the coffin.

Lee Magee

FIRST MEMORY
St. Patrick's Day 1994. I was up at the Parade on that day. My gold fish died. We buried him down the back garden. It was very sad to see him go.

SHELL
This shell reminds me of the pier.
It's like the noise of the sea.

AIR
It feels heavy.
It is vibration in the air that makes the winds.
It can make the waves rough.

I AM
I am the day my sister's house got built.
I am the day I was born.
I am the day I got my Holy Communion.
I am the day I got my new bike.

I am the day this dog followed me home and we kept him.

SPECIAL PERSON IN A NUTSHELL
My mummy and daddy are important to me, and grandad. Grandad was in the army. My daddy owns a bakery and my mummy owns a shop. And my uncle. He was in the First World War. He died in Belgium.

RED
Tastes like plastic.

WOOL
If you throw it up, it goes down slow.

BLACK
It smells like ink.
It feels rough.
It tastes like smoke.
It sounds like bees.
It reminds me of wood.

FIRST THINGS
I woke up this morning.
I smelled smoke.
I came to school.
When I reached the door
The air tasted of nothing.
I saw the Guards in their car this morning.

FIRE
Fire is red.
Fire reminds me of oil and diesel.
Fire is sitting on a candle-stick.
It smells like ashes.
The fire is like a blazing light.

Elaine McLaughlin

EARLIEST MEMORY
As far as I can remember is on the 15th August when my brother went on a Spanish trip with his friends to Omagh and a bomb had been planted there and my brother was killed. My brother's name was Shaun McLaughlin and a boy (eight) was killed too. His name was Oran. He lived four doors down. It was very hard to sleep then.

SHELL

It smells like crabs.

MY PLACE

My place is the Carn mountains because the noise is very quiet.
My place is the sight of Carndonagh.
My place is the road which is very bumpy.
My place is the way the driver gets tired.

OAT

It sounds like a pencil writing.
It feels like a pebble.

I AM

I am the day we did dance and movement. It got me fit.
I am the day of my first birthday.
I am the day of my Holy Communion.
I am the day I came to school.
I am the day my brother was born.
I am the day legs are important to you.

HAIKU

I did a project
I wrote about elephants.
It took me a day.

BLUE

I like blue
I'm getting my room done in it.
It looks like the sea.

WOOL

It looks like dog's hairs.
It smells like TCP.
It feels like cotton wool.
It reminds me of a pink dress.

FIRST THINGS

I saw the sun shining.
I heard the water tank.
I smelled toast.
I am glad it's Friday.

FIRE

Fire is very dangerous.
You should have a fireguard.

Keep young people away from it.
It is very sore if you get burned.
KEEP AWAY FROM FIRE.

Derek Doherty

EARLY MEMORY
My first pet was a cat. I called it Coal because it was black. I got it when it
was a kitten and now it is two years old and I've still got it now.

SHELL
The shell feels like a skull.
It tastes like sand.

FIRE
I like how the wax drops from the candle.
I like the yellow flame.
Every minute the candle gets smaller and smaller.
I like watching fire.

HERE COMES THE SUN
The sun is big and hot
It is like a big ball of lava
Coming crashing down.

AIR
It is like a big invisible cloud.

I AM
I am the time I got a medal for running.
I am the trophies I won.
I am the cat that I got.

WOOL
It looks like the hair of a doll.
It smells like sweets.
It tastes like dust.
It makes me think of knitting.

RESPONSE TO A POSTCARD
I am a cow. I am walking, running on the beach with my friend cows. I
don't know where we are going. I think a boy is looking after us, but he is
going into the water.

RED
It is bright and it is everywhere, it is danger and I like it.

Lee Stones

EARLY MEMORY
I was about four or five years old. I was having my dinner. When I finished my dinner I was getting out of the chair. I fell and hit my head off the ground. I was crying very hard. There was a bump on my head.

MY PLACE
My place is the house my granny and grandad Burns lived in. When I went to visit my granny and grandad Burns house, when I was going home my grandad always gave me and my brother and sister a pound, but now he can't do that because he died on the 17th December last year. My granny's still alive, but I'm not happy because my grandad died last year. My grandad was suffering. He was very sick.

AIR
Air smells of different things.
Air is soft.
Air whistles.
Air tastes like salt.

HAIKU
The winter is cold.
The winter is cold and dark.
Winter is snowing.

FIRST THINGS
I saw the cars go in and out of the car park.
The smell of dryness hit me when I walked in the school door.
I didn't feel good this morning.
I heard the horns of cars.
My orange tasted nice.

WOOL
It smells like a dirty onion.

RESPONSE TO A POSTCARD
I am fifty-six years of age. I use a walking stick. I live in Greece. It's hot here. I used to be a sailor. For 26 years. I had 39 men on board. We sailed all over the world. I have four drinks a week. The bar is good criac. I liked my life in the old days. My best restaurant is Jimmy's.

FIRE
Fire makes the wax on the candle burn like mad.
Fire is like the sun.

Fire is like an asteroid coming towards the earth.
Fire is the thing that makes you sweat.

Laura McConnell

BEST PERSON
My mother is very kind. She looks out for me and gives me a whole lot of things I probably don't deserve. My mother is from Dublin but moved up here when she met my Dad.

DREAM
My dream was about this man. He came to my house. I was in bed sleeping. As I woke up he was chasing me all around my house, the floor opened up and I was down in a type of dungeon. I tried to get away but he stopped me and then I woke up. I was really scared.

HERE COMES THE SUN
The sun had just come out on a beautiful summer day. No rain since yesterday. The clouds so puffy and soft. Soon the night will set in and the sun will go away.

AIR
Air has no shape.
Air is clear.

I AM
I am the day my brother was born.
I am the day I made my first Communion.
I am the day of my birthday.
I am the first day I got my dog.

Brenda Sheehy

FIRST MEMORY
I remember when I was five, I saw people climbing and swinging from trees, and I thought I could do that as well, so I climbed up the tree. I fell, but I was lucky I fell on my back, and didn't break anything, because it was a very tall tree. I went up to the house crying.

CLOVE
It smells like that stuff you take when you've got a tooth-ache.

I AM
The day when I first held my nephew.
The night that my brother and sister and I lay looking up at the stars.
The evening I heard my brother was getting married.
The summer when my sister played chase with me in the back of the house.
The time that I fell and my Mum was there to comfort me.
The time that my brother gave me a Boyzone ticket to go to a concert.

BLUE
It feels slippery.

FIRST THINGS
I smelled toast just made, that was black and burnt.
I saw my nephew with his pyjamas twisted, waking me up by hitting me on the bed.
I heard yawnings.
I tasted milky tea.

AIR
Air is shaking a Coke bottle and opening it so that the fizz comes up in your face.
Air is when you open a dirty nappy and the smell hits you.
Air is when you hold your breath for a minute and then breathe.
Air is the smell on a bus when you open the window.
Air keeps us alive.

WATER
It reminds me of pouring watered milk in a dish when the dog was a pup.

FIRE
Fire reminds me of a drawing I did with a candle in it.
It feels as if it is going to fall.
It smells like a burnt roast.
It makes me think of Christmas morning when I go to Mass.
It makes me feel peaceful.

Clare McLaughlin

FIRST MEMORY
I remember my first day at play school. My mammy came in with me. I started crying. I grabbed hold of my mammy. I wouldn't let go. The teacher had to pull me off. After a little while I calmed down. The same thing happened to me when I started this school, too.

149

CLOVE
It smells like clove rock.
I've seen it in my granny's whiskey or brandy.
It looks like a little seed with a long tail.

MY PLACE IS
My place is my home. You are never lonely, because you have neighbours.
My place is close to a hotel.
My place is close to a shop.
My place is where I have my own bedroom.

SPRING HAIKU
I like planting plants.
Flowers grow in the spring days.
Some grow in winter.

ART HAIKU
Drawing is good fun.
You can draw funny pictures.
I like drawing things.

MY BEST DAY
My best day was my birthday last year. I had a party and presents and
money. Then a few days after that we went to Derry. I brought some of
my money with me but my mummy held onto it for me in case I lost it. I
bought my own clothes and a pair of shoes.

EGG
It looks like a little pond with an orange ball in it.
You can hear the cracks of it when you fry it.

WHITE
White is the colour of incense.
White is the colour of my sheet.

FIRE
Fire keeps you warm at night.
It can also cause accidents.
It is a fearsome thing.
It won't stop at anything.
When you put your finger though it, it doesn't hurt.

WATER
It sounds like a clock ticking.

Michael Reid

RED
Red looks like the sun shining on the sea.
Red tastes like apples ripe off the tree.
Red is the fire burning when you smell the smoke.
Red is the sun's warmth.

I AM
I am the first time I learned to play football. I have been playing ever since.
I am the day I first went to school. I met my friends.
I am the day when Ireland got into the World Cup. I was delighted.
I am the day my brother was born.
I am the day I split my eye.

WORST DAY
I've never really had a terrible day, but plenty of bad ones. One of these
was when I fell down the stairs and twisted my ankle. The only good thing
about it was that I was off school for three days. Another bad day was
when I got the chicken-pox. I was scratching like mad.

BLUE
Blue is a sky with birds.
Blue is very light.

EGG
It looks like a lump of yellow jelly surrounded in clear slime.
It sizzles on the pan, spitting and changing colour.

FIRST THINGS
I smelled a hot cup of tea.
I saw the grey clouds in the sky.
I tasted a slice of scone.
I felt my warm bed. I didn't want to get up.

ORANGE
Orange is the sun's warmth.
Orange feels soft and cosy.
It reminds me of an egg yolk.
It smells like chips out of a chip shop.
It tastes hot and greasy.

I HAVE A DREAM
I had a dream that my family and I were shopping, and terrorists came in

and held everyone hostage. There were four of them. One had a glass eye. One had a Halloween suit on. The other two had masks. I still hadn't noticed yet, and was walking around shops when I tripped and woke up.

RESPONSE TO MUSIC
It's a soft, sad and gentle song. It made me feel a little bit sad. There was complete silence in the room when the song was played.

FIRE
Looks like it is dancing on the candle, moving from side to side.
It makes water boil and bubble.

AIR
Air is all around us.
When air is mad it turns into wind.

Conor Fullerton

FIRST MEMORY
I remember I was walking along the edge of the Mill River. I fell and slipped on a rock and went into the river. I was very wet and my mummy was very cross with me.

I AM
The day I went on my holidays to Westport. I was really excited.
The day I split my head. It was very sore.
The morning my brother was born.
The day I went to hospital with a sore leg.
The day of my aunty's wedding.
The day my cousin died.

WHITE
White is the taste of milk.
The sound of hailstones.
It has the feel of cotton.
It looks like snow on the ground.
My hair is white.

YELLOW
Yellow is the hot fire in my sitting-room.
It's the heat in the sun.
It smells bitter.
It tastes like lemon juice.

WORST DAY
One of the worst days of my life was when I was going down Knockalla Bray on a skateboard. I hit the kerb and fell and split my head.

I HAVE A DREAM
I have a dream to play for Aston Villa or Celtic.
I have a dream that my cousin Oran could be alive again. He died in the Omagh bombing.

EGG
It looks like a yellow bubble in a puddle of slime.
It smells a bit like a bar of soap.
It makes a cracking sound when you are putting it in the pan.
I like to put my egg in the microwave, or boil it.

FIRST THINGS
I heard the birds singing in the early morning.
I tasted sugar puffs as I sat on the sofa watching TV.
I watched the birds flying and coming back again.
I felt the fabric of my blanket in bed.
I saw my mummy cooking a fry for my daddy.

I HAD A DREAM
That I was being chased by two viscious hounds when I was about six or seven. And everywhere I went more dogs were there. I woke my mummy and daddy I was crying so loud. For the next few nights I had the same dream again and again. All this was not a dream but a nightmare.

TIME HAIKU
Seconds and seconds
Minutes and minutes go by
This is precious time.

FIRE
Fire feels like the heat in my sitting-room at night.
It smells like smoke from my chimney mixing with the fresh air.
It looks yellowish orange.
It makes a crackling sound when water is poured on it.
I like to lie in front of the hot fire, but after a few minutes I move because it's too hot.

EARTH
Earth is soundless, but it can burst your ear-drums in an avalanche.
Earth looks like when my mum used to crumble a biscuit and put it on ice-cream.

Worms live in earth.

WATER

Water keeps us alive.
Water relaxes me in a hot bath.

Declan Fullerton

I REMEMBER

I remember when I was small and I broke my leg. I had to go to hospital. I was lying in bed nearly all day. I had to get a bandage on my leg. Every day I kept trying to walk but I found it too hard. It took a long time for my leg to get better.

I AM

I am the day that I won two trophies and was very proud.
I am the day that I started school.
I am the day when it was my birthday and I went to Manchester.
I am the day that I first made friends.
I am the day when I had my first operation. I was a bit scared.
I am the day I went to America.

STRAW

It looks like the string of a guitar.
It reminds me of the summer when I am going to play football in the park.

BLUE

Blue is the sound of the wind.
It reminds me of winter when I go out to throw snowballs.
It sounds like a freezing winter night.

MY BEST DAY

It was my birthday on 23rd April, and my daddy told me I was going to see Manchester Utd. play football. At the end of the whole trip, Manchester won 5-0 against Nottingham Forest. I never forget that day. It was the best birthday present I ever got.

I HAVE A DREAM

I had a dream that I fell into a river and nearly drowned. I kept swimming and swimming and the waves kept splashing into my face. A couple of people saw me and tried to save me. I was very scared. I saw a few rocks coming towards me and I grabbed onto them. Someone threw a float into the river and I swam and got it. It was not good enough for me and I was heading for a waterfall and

I just woke up.

RESPONSE TO MUSIC
It sounds like someone playing the guitar in the middle of the street.
It makes me think of when I get up on Christmas morning.

EARTH
It looks like mushed-up chocolate.
It reminds me of when I'm walking on a farm.

FIRE
Fire reminds me of when I'm sitting in the house on a Saturday night, in front of the fire, watching TV.
It feels tickly on your finger.
I see it every Sunday when I am at Mass.
If I look close at it I think of the sun.
I don't really like the smell of fire.

Patrick Doherty

FIRST MEMORY
I remember my first day at school. I started to cry because I didn't want to leave my mummy, so mummy said to me, *If I give you 50p will you stop crying?* I said *Yes.* I enjoyed my first day of school.

GOLD
Looks shiny and feels smooth.
It sounds like a heavy book falling on the table.
It smalls like Cidona.
HAY
It looks like a long gold piece of string.

MY BEST DAY
Was when I went to Waterworld in Bundoran. I cut my foot in the whirlpool.
On the way home we went into a shopping centre and bought things.

I HAVE A DREAM
To play for Liverpool.

BROWN
Brown is the smell of bark off a tree.

Brown is the taste of Rolos.
Brown looks like the walls of an old house.

FIRST THINGS
This morning I saw the Mill River.
This morning I tasted my breakfast.
This morning I heard my brother snoring.
This morning I felt cold when I went outside.

FIRE
Fire smells like smoke from a burning house.
Fire sounds like cracking wood.
Fire tastes like a hot dinner on a cold day.
Fire looks like a flame on a stick.
AIR
Air tastes like a freezing cold dinner.

WATER
Sounds like rain hitting against the window. It feels loose and cold.

Cahal O'Sullivan

EGG
It smells like fart gas.
It looks like an eye.
It tastes of cheese.
It has no sound.
It feels like jelly,
Which reminds me of when I hit
My head and forehead
My skull, and the hole in my head
Felt like jelly.
FIRST MEMORY
I remember when I was six years old I had to go to hospital to get my tonsils
out. I was stuck in the hospital bed for ages because the nurse gave me too
much anaesthetic. I was in the bed for two-and-a-half weeks asleep. Then I
remember people coming to visit me, and I remember going home.

FIRST THINGS
I used my sight to see my dog with a friend he brought home.
I used my taste to taste the creaminess of the milk.

I used my touch to get dressed this morning.
I used my hearing to hear the radio.
I used my smell to smell the toast burning.

I HAVE A DREAM

I had a dream that I went to America and stayed with my uncle. He brought me to Disneyland. I remember eating an orange ice-lolly. When I woke up I could taste orange in my mouth.

TIME

Why does time fly?
Time? Where does it go?

EARTH

Earth is so powerful.
Earth is what we stand on every day.

Dean Crumlish

I REMEMBER

I remember being on my holidays in Dublin. I stayed in a big house. We went out every day to the shops. My mammy and daddy were there too and we stayed for three days.

CLOVE

When I nibbled it, it tasted spicy and hot.
I've seen them on oranges as well.

MY PLACE

My place is the tree outside my house, which is great for climbing.
My place is the garden, which is great for playing.
My place is the field, which is good for hiding.

I AM

I am the night my daddy was on TV.
I am the time my brother and I had the house to ourselves.
I am the evening that was boring because my mummy and daddy were away.

HAY

It feels like threads.
It smells like the attic.
Some bits looks like hair,
And I've seen it on farms, all stacked up.

SILVER

Silver is the smell of sweat.
It tastes like rust.
It sounds like metal.
It's like a flash of lightning around the clouds.

BLACK

Feels like coal.
Black smells like burnt toast.
Black looks like tar.
Black sounds like a bomb.
Black tastes like a Black Jack.

RESPONSE TO MUSIC

It smells like soap from the pack and sounds like the sea on a windy night
and tastes like strawberries covered in sugar and I don't like it.

FIRE

I've seen it when the power goes out.
It reminds me of lava exploding from a volcano.
It smells like a bonfire.

AIR

Air is a nippy wind in winter.
We breathe it every two seconds.
It reminds me of gas when I put on tea.

EARTH

I used to play with it when I was wee.

WATER

It's cold on your hand and I use it to wake up every morning and I like to
drink it and it reminds me of the pool.

Carolanne Doherty

CLOVE

When I was young my neighbour was drinking whisky with these in it. I
took a sip when he was gone and I spat the drink out everywhere.
It feels like the top of an apple.

PURPLE

Looks like royalty.

It tastes like the stone in a plum.
It smells like a dried-up rose.

BARLEY
It smells like when you enter a field of corn or wheat.
It tastes like every morning when I eat my porridge.
It sounds like when you make a mistake and try to rub it out with a rubber.

I AM
I am the day I went to the hospital to get my appendix out.
I am the day my brother and my best friend and I made a little hut.
I am the first time I learnt how to cycle.
I am the day I split my leg.
I am the first day at school.
I am the first day I was allowed to walk in the town by myself.
I am the day I met Boyzone.

HAY
It smells like my great uncle's old farm.
It feels like a few strings of grass hauled together.
It sounds like the wind blowing over a bush.
The last time I saw it I was rolling about in it.

RED
Red is the colour of danger, love and the sun on a sizzling hot day.
It has a passionate resistance.
It is the colour of my school uniform.
It looks fierce.

HAIKU
Outside at my break
I watch the birds eating food
That we left behind.

FIRE
Fire reminds me of the first big fire my dad was trying to fight at my next-door neighbour's.
It reminds me of the time of the Omagh bomb.
I had really scary nightmares of fire where I was trapped and couldn't get out of the house.
It reminds me of heartburn.
It feels like your stomach's on fire.

AIR
It reminds me of the times I smelt the fresh haunting scent out on my uncle's farm.

WATER
I find that when I drink water, it makes me a little dizzy for a second.

Paul McNutt

FIRST MEMORY
I remember the first time I played golf. I hit the ball into the sand trap. It took me five shots to get it out. It took me ten shots to get it in the hole. I was six years old.

BARLEY
It looks like peeled-off skin with veins.

I AM
I am the day my granda and granny were in a car crash.
I am the day we went to America. The heat just hit us.
I am the day I split my head while playing outside my house.

BEST DAY
The best day that I had was when we were going to Chicago. It took us four hours to get to Dublin. When we boarded the plane we got a salad. After four hours we got our dinner and it was pasta. After eight hours we were finally there. My uncle and aunty collected us and we stayed for three weeks. After a couple of weeks, I got sunburn.

EGG
Looks like an eye-ball.

GREY
Is as thick as fog.
Grey sounds like someone lighting a fire.
Grey is the colour of your hair when it is old.

FIRST THINGS
I smelled my breakfast being cooked.
I heard my spoon dropping.

CURRANT
It feels squishy and spongy.
It looks like tiny grains.

RESPONSE TO MUSIC
It sounds sad and gentle.

It looks like a sad little boy.

I HAVE A DREAM

I have a dream that I was alone in the world. When I got out of bed, my mum did not come down with my breakfast. After a little while I went to school. There was no-one there but teachers. It was scary, and when I got into my class, the door closed tightly and there was a teacher who made me do work. I did every subject but sums. When I finished the first sum, I woke up and there was my mum with my breakfast.

FIRE

We held candles on the night of my friend's wake.

AIR

Air is the thing that we thrive on.

WATER

I've seen it on my face.
Water is the thing we drink.
I've seen water flowing through Mill River.
Water is what you boil in a kettle to make tea. I drink tea every morning.
I don't like water very much, but I drink it anyway.

Claire Hegarty

CLOVE

It feels like a star on a stick.

MY PLACE

The thing I think that is special about our school is that we have able and disabled and we are all treated the same.

FIRST MEMORY

I remember when I had to get eight teeth out in the hospital because I would not go to the dentist. There was a horrible smell and I had to wait very long until I could see the doctor. And when I went in he asked me to lie down and put a mask on me and knocked me out. When I got up I could not speak or do anything because they gave me too much gas and I felt terrible for a week.

I AM

I am the day I went to hospital.

I am the day my baby brothers were born.
I am the days I used to fight with my sisters.
I am the days when I used to fall and cut my knees.
I am the day I won an Easter egg in Miss O'Hare's.
I am the day I used to go to Feises with big flowery dresses.
I am the day I went to Omagh on 15th August.

BLUE

It looks like a crystal ball.
Blue is the colour of my eyes.

HAY

It reminds me of the grass at the Old People's Home before it got cut.
I saw it in the farm next door to my granny's and granda's.
It feels like a little spider crawling up you.

BEST DAY/WORST DAY

My worst day was the day I went to Omagh. It was very scary.
My best days were when I used to play around my park.
My best day was when I could cycle my bicycle.
My worst days were when I was sick.
My worst day was when I had to go to hospital.
My best day was when I went to meet Boyzone.

EGG

Egg looks like a piece of jelly with a yellow ball in the middle.
Egg reminds me of the time when my first Spaniard came and made me a Spanish omlette.
I always get eggs up in my granny's and granda's at Easter.

PINK

It looks like a pink bow.
It sounds like a baby girl was born.
It reminds me of little girls in the summer.

CURRANT

It smells like the fruit cakes my granny makes.

RESPONSE TO MUSIC

It makes me think of poor children over in poor countries.
It makes me feel lucky.

FIRE

I am sometimes afraid of fire.

I don't like it.

AIR

Air is what we are surrounded with.
Air is a thing we cannot see.
Air gives us life.
We need air or else we will suffocate.

EARTH

It smells like my granny's garden.
It looks like crumbs of a chocolate biscuit.

WATER

I always drink it after I play football.
When you let it fall down your hand it looks like a tear going down someone's cheek.

HAIKU

I wish there was a
Bridge of music because I
Would walk it all day

FIRE

Fire looks like a light bulb.
It reminds me of the time the remains of the three boys who died in the
Omagh bomb, came home.
I always think of life when the candle is lit, and death when it goes out.

Fergal Barber

AIR

Air is an element.
Air is the wind.

WORD POEM

A dictionary
And a Thesaurus
Have lots of words.

FIRE

It reminds me of the time I was sitting in the sitting room of my house watching the Late, Late Toy Show with the fire glowing around the room.

EGG

It feels slippery and wet.
It sounds like saying *Yes*.

YELLOW
It looks like the school buses.
It sounds like a flame burning on top of a candle.

CURRANT
It tastes like a dried grape.

HAIKU
I hate school class work.
I have a dictionary.
My name is Fergal.

HAY
I saw it on the floor of my aunty's stable.
It sounds like a match being run between your fingers.
It smells of cows.

BEST DAY
My best day was when I was in fourth class. I didn't think I was going to
win first prize in the school draw. My prize was a cake and an Easter egg.

I HAVE A DREAM
That I could flip and somersault.
I have a dream that I was a famous inventor even.

FIRST MEMORY
First thing I remember was at my brother Brendan's christening in 1988.

MY PLACE
The special thing about my room is that my bed is in it.

Mary Flanagan

EGG
It looks like the sun surrounded by a cloud.
It feels creamy and thick.
It sounds snappy and crackly.
It smells like the chicken farms in Donegal.
It tastes like the eggs we get in a fry on Sunday.
I have seen it in the frying pan, lying sizzling.
It reminds me of a fog with the moon looking through it.

BABY BLUE
It is the smell of a crocus in spring.

It's the sound of the birds at dawn.
It tastes like an ice-cube.
It feels like water surrounding a deserted island.
It makes me think of a dolphin jumping.
It makes me feel cold.
I've seen it a lot in my mind.

I AM

I am the day of my sister's wedding where I was pulled right through the
crowd onto the dance floor in my flower-girl dress.
I am the day I fell out of the car door and when I came home my mum
was peeling the potatoes.
I am the Christmases when all my relations come.
I am the days all my family and cousins and aunties and uncles and
grannies would go to the beach from 11am to 8pm.
I am the day when my first nephew was born and seeing him in his cot
with his swarthy skin sleeping.
I am the day my niece was being born. I was in suspense, would it be a
boy or a girl?

FIRST MEMORY

I remember when I was about five, I tripped on the fire grate in the sitting-
room and fell on a stone lion which had a pointy bit. It was a very deep
cut and I remember feeling scared and shocked. It went into my head
above my eye-brow. There is still a scar there.

I HAVE A DREAM

That people will stop abortion. They say that children are dying all over the
world. It is the exact same thing because you are killing a baby, a child, an adult,
a grand-parent. It is more or less saying someone has the right to kill someone.
World hunger is hard to stop, but if this can be stopped why not do it?

WORST DAY

The worst day was when I fell out of the car. With the lock down I felt
secure, but when daddy swung the car around before parking, the door
swung open and the feeling of dropping - your heart lifts and you feel as if
you are never going to stop falling. I never cried. I suppose it was just shock.

MY GOOD DAY

Was when we made a snowman about ten foot high. We had to use a ladder
to build it. We put a cowboy hat on the top of it. I remember people going
past and throwing stones and things at it, but nobody could knock it down.

Eventually the strong power of the sun melted the enormous snowman.

PINK
It is the feeling you get when a baby would be soothed from its crying.
It's the sound of a hand running through silk.
It's the smell of the colour of the sun coming through the curtains in the morning.

RED
It tastes like an ice-cube so cold that there's steam coming from it.
It sounds like the wind getting through a tiny crack in a window.
It reminds me of the beating of a drum with hands.

I HAVE A DREAM
I have a dream that my cousin Aisling wasn't gone. She had a brilliant sense of humour. Lovely long curly ginger hair. She was only nineteen when she died of leukaemia. I remember seeing her in the coffin. She looked so pale. I remember being afraid to touch her. Once I saw another person touch her, I finally brought myself to touch her hand. It felt so cold. I remember seeing her for the last time the night before she died. She was so weak and could barely talk. I remember her saying *What's the criac?* That was the last thing I can remember her saying. She died the next day.

TIME HIAKU
Everything takes time:
To be born, to live, to die.
Time always goes fast.

FIRE
Fire overpowers you with its warm, striking power.
It reminds me of Easter, when the priest would walk to the altar with a candle held high in the air.
Fire is weak against the power of the wind.
It's like a tulip closed for the night.
Then it dies.

AIR
It's the stale and clean thing we breathe.

Jonathan Friel

I REMEMBER
When I was rushed into hospital that night. I was in pain for four hours before I saw the doctor, and then I had to wait another half hour before I got

a bed. The pain was getting worse, then the doctor diagnosed it as an ulcer.

CLOVE

It sounds like someone clicking their fingers.
It looks like a dinosaur's foot.

MY PLACE IS

The main plant of Fruit of the Loom, in Buncrana.
My place is the golf course which is brilliant.

GREEN

Green is sticky when you touch it.
It is the colour of the roll book.
It sounds like a cork dropping.

I AM

I am the day my friends Shaun and Oran died.
I am the day Tony Blair and John Hume were in my next-door neighbour's house. All the policemen were outside.

HAY

It smells like the country-side.
It feels like thread.
I have seen it on a cottage roof.

ORANGE

It looks like the sun setting on a hot evening.
It tastes like the carrots I force into me every Sunday.

BEST DAY/WORST DAY

My worst day was when I found out that Shaun and Oran died.
My best day was Christmas morning when I got my first set of golf clubs.
A bad day was when I broke my three wood which I got for Christmas.

RESPONSE TO MUSIC

It sounds like a lady talking but putting it into a song.
It makes me feel like the lady loves a man but she can't say it in words.
It feels gentle, like you're putting your head on a soft woolly pillow.

FIRE

Fire reminds me of a cold winter's night when my dad puts the fire on and if you close the door quickly, all the fire comes out of the fire-place and makes a bad smell.

Christopher Doherty

FIRST MEMORY

I remember when I went to the zoo. I was three years old. First we went to the restaurant. I fell asleep for about two hours. The first animal I saw was the polar bear. It was swimming in the water.

AIR

The field beside me is very stinky and I always hold my breath passing it.

RED

Red smells like a bad apple.

I AM

I am the day I fell in the river.
I am the day when I ran away. I remember it most.

BLUE

Blue feels rough.
Blue tastes like bubble gum.

BEST DAY

My best day was when I went to Bundoran where the waves were splashing.

I HAVE A DREAM

I have a dream that the world was peaceful.
I have a dream that I could go to Celtic and see them play.
I had a dream that I fell in a river. Two days after that, I did.
I had a nightmare that I had two heads.

GOLD

Gold looks shiny as a fish's scale.
Gold smells sweet.
Gold feels hard.
Gold sounds like money rattling on metal.
Gold tastes like toast.

FIRST THINGS

I felt sad because I had to go to school.
I heard my mummy saying *Get Up*.
I looked dead as a Dodo.
I tasted toast. It felt hot.

Emma Lawrence

FIRST MEMORY

The very first thing I remember is my daddy coming home from hospital in a wheelchair. His eye had been taken out, just for half a month, though it still upset me. Then daddy said he had something like multiple sclerosis. He was just in the wheelchair for a while. But now he's in it permanently. He can't do everything everybody else's dad does, but he's still my dad. He got hurt when a tree fell on him at work. He was in the army. Then they put his eye back in. I wasn't born when he got hurt, but I remember him being on a stick, but now he's in the wheelchair.

MY PLACE IS

My place is down in Swan Park. My brother and I go fishing there. But he moved to England. I have photos of us fishing and one day I wore my best velvet blue dress down and I fell in. When he comes home we always go fishing. I really enjoy it.

I AM

I am the day I was flower-girl in my brother's wedding in a cream and green dress.
I am the morning I was rushed into hospital and put on two drips.
I am the evening my granny died. My sister fainted.
I am the day my nephew was born. I was crying with joy.
I am the night I fell down the stairs and split my head. I had to get four stitches.
I am the day my god-father nearly got his fingers cut off at work.
I am the evening my cousin was born at 1lb weight. He was tiny.

RED

Is the taste of strawberries
Is the smell of wool
Sounds like the hot coal singeing
It makes me feel warm

Rachel Farrell

I REMEMBER

I remember when I got my first bike for Christmas.
I remember when my grandfather died.
I can remember when my mummy broke her arm.
I remember when my brother fell off the tractor and hurt himself badly.
I remember when I was young I split my leg and had to stay in hospital for

a good while. I was very afraid. A lot of people came to see me. All I thought about was getting home.

I can remember when I went to the river with my friend. I was at the edge of the water when someone pushed me in.

The best thing I like about going to my granny's house is to look at all the mountains.

ORANGE

It smells like the peel of an orange.
It sounds like the water running from a tap.
It looks like when the sun goes down.

I AM

I am the day when my mummy was having my baby brother.
I am the day when I got my first bike.
I am the day I made my Holy Communion.
I am the day when I went to my cousin's wedding.
I am the day when I went to Cork.
I am the day when my granda died.
I am the day when it was my birthday.
I am the day of my brother's christening.

SILVER

Looks like the stars.
Silver feels like the wind.
Silver smells like spoons and forks.
Silver sounds like the stars.

RESPONSE TO MUSIC

It sounds sweet and gentle.
It reminds me of poor children.
It makes me feel like crying.

I HAVE A DREAM

I had a dream about when I was walking on the beach and I could hear footsteps coming behind me. I looked around but there was no-one there. I could see footprints in the sand, which was terrifying. Suddenly I felt something hitting me. I looked, but there was nobody there. I went into the water for a paddle. I could see a shadow in the water. It was saying *Come here at once.* I was that terrified that I woke up. I let a scream out of me, and my mum and dad raced up the stairs like thunder. I was so glad it was not true.

Bridgeen Grant

I AM
I am the day I made my First Communion.
I am the afternoon I fell and hit the door and split my forehead.
I am the day I went to school.
I am the day of my birthday.

HAY
I have seen it in horses' stables.

RED
Red is the colour of blood.
Red is the colour of the sunset.

BEST DAY/WORST DAY
My best day was when I made my first Holy Communion. I wore a long white dress.
My bad day was the day when my friend was at my house and my daddy was at work. My mammy was making the dinner. I came running in from the back and hit my head on the door and I had to have six stitches.

EGG
It looks like jelly.
It feels like slime.
It has a clear white and a yellow yolk.

CURRANT
It feels like wrinkled skin.

David Gallivan

FIRST MEMORY
I remember when I was in England with my mummy and daddy, we were on a bus and I fell and hurt my knee. I was staying with my godparents. They had cats and a little sand box so I could play.

MY PLACE
The smell of my place is a smell of spring.
The sound of birds sing my place.

RED

Red is the taste of red lemonade.
Red is like a snake on your table.

I AM

I am the time I fell off my shed roof.
I am the time I burnt my finger, it was very sore.
I am the day I almost got knocked down. I am the time my cousin died.
She was almost one year. Her name was Megan.

FIRST THINGS

I smell my breakfast cooking.
I look at my two cats sleeping.
I hear two birds singing in a tree.
I taste my milk for my breakfast.

BLUE

Blue smells like pen ink.
Blue looks like a cloud in a good day.

I HAD A DREAM

That I was on a football team. I was playing for Liverpool and I was forward. There was only one defender. I got past him and he ran up behind me and hacked me. That was the nightmare because then I lost my leg.
Then I woke up and looked at my leg. It was still there.

TIME

The game we were playing was What Time Is It Mr. Wolf?
It is time for Liverpool to beat Man United.
It is time
It is time
It's bed time.

Ciaran McGory

FIRST MEMORY

When I was one I had asthma and my daddy took me up to the hospital.
When I was outside the hospital, my daddy pulled the hand brake and my finger came off.

HOMEWORK

I hate homework.
My mummy tells me to do homework
And I am to sit there for an hour each day.

BLUE

Smells like something rotting.

I AM

I am the day I got knocked down.
I am the day my finger came off.
I am the day I was at my cousin's wedding.
I am the day the spokes of the bike cut my fingers.

SILVER

When I see silver it reminds me of money.
Silver looks like metal shining.
Silver smells like trouble.
Silver tastes like bins.

RESPONSE TO MUSIC

It sounds like a very sad song.
It feels like someone is leaving her.
It smells like she's having a bad day.
It reminds me of my cousin.

I HAD A DREAM

I had a dream that we were attacked by aliens.
I had a dream that I was in Derry and got lost.
I had a dream that someone was trying to kill me.
I had a dream that I was rich.
I had a dream that there were no wars.

FIRE

Sounds like an egg cooking.
Fire tastes like an atomic fireball.

AIR

Smells like chocolate.

WATER

Water sounds like a pan boiling.

HAY

It feels like a wire.
It smells like rushes.
I've seen it before - cows eat it.

David Grant

I REMEMBER

I remember when I jumped over my wall. I hurt my leg and I could not walk for a few days.

MY PLACE

My place is my bedroom because it has a Play Station in it and it is the smallest bedroom in the house.

GREEN

Green tastes like Seven Up.
Green looks like grass after being cut.

I AM

I am the day that I fell in the mud.
I was all mud. I had to go and change my clothes.
I am the day I got my tonsils out. I did not want to get them out.

BLUE

Blue looks like a summer's day.
My bed quilt has blue in it.

MY BEST DAY

My best day was Christmas. I got three computer games.
My best day was when I got my Chelsea top.

FOOTBALL HAIKU

I support Celtic
They are the best team ever,
Wearing green and white.

EGG

It looks like a giant's eye.
It sounds like jelly.

ORANGE

It reminds me of the butt of a cigarette.

FIRE

Fire is very very dangerous.
It reminds me of the sun.
I saw it at Mass.
Fire is red and yellow.

EARTH

Earth - we walk on earth.

WATER

Reminds me of the pool.
There is more water in the world than land.

Aoife Deeney

FIRST MEMORY

I remember when I was about four - I had a brand new dress. I was playing with my friend over beside the river. Some boys were there and I remember them getting little red berries called itchybacks and they threw them down my dress. My back was really itchy after that. No matter how many times I washed the dress, it was still always itchy, so I never wore the dress again.

CLOVE

It tastes like dentists' gloves.
I have seen them in my granny's house in a big jar.

MY PLACE

My place is the big tree at the top of the road. My friends and I play up there. When we were small we played hotel. Now we just sit and talk. We each have three branches and there are two look-outs. In the autumn we used to dress in clothes that would hide us in the leaves. One summer day we had a picnic up there. It isn't dangerous because it hangs over the grass.

I AM

I am the day I read at my cousin's wedding.
I am the day my grand aunt died.
I am the day I found out that I was going to be an aunty.
I am the day I was going to swim in the All-Ireland competition.
I am the evening my two friends and I went down to the Stone Jug and watched the sun-set.

WORST DAY/ BEST DAY

A bad day for me was when I had to go to hospital to get a tooth out. It was scary. I was about four years old. I was gassed and put to sleep. When I woke up I felt really dizzy. When I got out of the hospital I ate a big tub of ice-cream and I felt much better.

My best day was when I was at Mosney at the All-Ireland Swimming Competition. I felt nervous and I had butterflies in my stomach, but I had a feeling of exactness inside of me also.

HAIKU

In 1066
At the Battle of Hastings
William won the war.

HAY

It looks like a piece of hair that hasn't been brushed for a few days. It reminds me of when I did a play in the Little Angels School in Letterkenny.

EGG

It looks like a flying saucer.
It looks like a castle with a moat.

PINK

Pink smells sweet like a tulip.
It looks like a baby girl's blanket.
It tastes like a marshmallow.

FIRST THINGS

I smelt a musty smell on the priest's cloak at Mass.
I saw my sister's French notes for her exam.
I felt Communion this morning at 7.30 Mass.
I tasted grapefruit for my breakfast.

RESPONSE TO MUSIC

I don't know why, but the song makes me think of my old cat that died.
I don't think Marian Bradfield sounds from Donegal.

I HAVE A DREAM

Every time I get the flu I have the same dream. It's about a boy who gets killed by an aeroplane. It's very weird.

Is mise Aoife

Ta conaí orm in Eirinn
Is maith liom Eire.

FIRE

One time when I was sick my friends went to the beach, and a fire started.
The heather started it.
It reminds me of the time when my friends and I went up the street when
the bodies of the victims of the Omagh bomb came back.

AIR

What is air?
I mean no-one can hear it, no-one can feel it, no-one can see it or smell it
or taste it. Yet we can't live without it. Everything and everyone needs it
to live. Air is a very strange thing.

EARTH

It smells like my granny's gardening gloves.
It reminds me of a bag of compost.

Daryl Kelly

I REMEMBER

I remember when I put chocolate all over my uncle's face when I was
about three. Then he lifted me up and gave me to my mother. It was
awful. I did not get a bar for about a week.
The place I like is the Liverpool Stadium. I like it because when you are
going to your seat, everybody is singing and cheering as loud as they can.

BLUE

It is the summer sea and the sky early in the morning.

HAY

It feels like someone pulling a soft wire through your fingers.

YELLOW

Yellow is the colour of the moonlit night
And the sun in the morning.
Yellow is the flowers that grow in the green grass.

WATER

It comes from rivers.
It cleans your body.

It helps you get up in the morning.
It is water that you drink.

BRIDGE HAIKU
I went past a bridge
I went past a bridge today
I went past a bridge.

AIR
Air - we cannot see it.
It is clear.

Rosemary Maloney

FIRST MEMORY
I remember going up to a man called David. He owned ten horses and a
donkey called Cindy. I sometimes go with my dog and brother. David's
sister gave me a sugar lump and I gave it to Flash. I love horses. Flash
was grey and blue. He was in a small field.

MY PLACE IS
The horses up at my house.
My place is the two dogs - Sam running and Bruno walking.
My place is the workman coming up the drive.
My place is the kettle on for a cup of tea and some food.
My place is the book to read.

BLUE
Blue feels like blackberry juice.
Blue is a good book.
Blue sounds like water going up and down in a bottle.
Blue feels round like a hen.

I AM
I am the day I went to Mary Nichols'. She had two horses but now she has
three.
I am the day I got my dog Sam. My Dad's friend came and we went up to get
him. He was white as chalk. He went mental when he saw me.

RED
Red looks like blood.
It reminds me of a jump.
I have seen it on a North-West bus my Dad designed.

It sounds like a ring falling.

I HAVE A DREAM

I have a dream of being a vet because I love animals, or to be a helper in the vet's room.
I have a dream of adopting a dolphin in America.

EGG

It is sloppy.
I have seen it when my mum is making bread.

BLACK

Black is the colour of the sky at night.
Black reminds me of the writer's dog.
I see black writing in books.

FIRST THINGS

This morning I smelt the dogs.
I heard my dog Sam run up and down the hall.
I felt my duvet.

RESPONSE TO MUSIC

It sounds like birds flying past.
It makes me feel I am in a garden and I am all alone.

TIME HAIKU

Time goes fast each day
I use time every day
What is time about?

FIRE

Is the colour of my jumper when it's just been washed.

Noeleen O'Donnell

FIRST MEMORY

I remember when I had to go for a check-up. When I got back out to the car my mum told me I had to go to hospital for an operation. My stomach started to feel all funny. I felt as if I was going to get sick. It was three days until my operation, and those days went by very fast. When the day came I was really nervous. On my first day in hospital, I just got settled in. Then the day for the operation came. I remember going into a white bright room. For a few minutes everything was quiet. After that everything went black. After a few hours I woke up. The nurse was saying I would be O.K. I went back to my room. I was very dizzy. The next day I went home. The only thing I could think about was that I was glad it was over.

MY PLACE IS
My place is the shore front at Easter and summer holidays. There is always a funfair. And if there is no funfair you can always play on the swings and slides.

SILVER
Silver sounds like tingling wind chimes.
Looks like the moon shining on the water.
Feels like something cold and sharp.

I AM
The day I won my first medal.
The night I first started piano.
The first time I was on a stage acting.
I am the time when I did my first Feis and concert.
I am the first time I received Holy Communion.
I am the day when I first started school.
I am the day when I got my tonsils out.

HAY
I have seen it on a trip through my uncle's field.
It reminds me of a straw basket.

RED
It reminds me of the dark red chalk crumbling on a piece of black paper.

HAIKU
I played in the park
I spotted piles of rubbish
I picked it all up.

EGG
Egg looks like lots of buttercups without the stems.
On the outside it looks like someone painted whitewash around them.

FIRST THINGS
When I woke up I felt very dizzy, so I just fell back down on the pillows.
I tasted a hot crusty criossant.
When I walked to the door I saw a bunch of stems standing up tall, as if

they were very proud of something.
I saw the trees waving over and back as if they were waving at me.

RESPONSE TO MUSIC
I felt sad when I heard the start of the song.
It reminded me of all my sad and bad memories.
It made me think of people who had no-one to look after them.
It reminded me of my granny's burial and I was throwing a dark red rose
into the grave.

AIR
Air helps us to breathe.
I love it when I walk and the air is blowing up against my face, and my hair
is blowing everywhere.

FIRE
Fire looks like a gold star in the dark.
It reminds me of eating curry.
Every time I hear the Fire Brigade, I think of someone trying to get out of
a house surrounded by fire.

WATER
Water is crystal clear.
If water is on your palm and you blow at it, you can see the little ripples.
When I look out of my bedroom window on a calm day, I always think I
can walk across the water on the beach without it going over my head.

Danielle McGonigle

FIRST MEMORIES
I remember my brother's christening. I sang on stage by myself.
I remember my first time on a boat. I thought I was going to drown, and
closed my eyes the whole way round.
I remember when I was five a dog bit me, and I went over to pet it again.
I remember when I was wee and I went into hospital and I was afraid of
the black doctors, and I was crying the whole time.
At the top of the lane is my granny's house, then my uncle's house, then
my aunty's house, then my house.

PURPLE
It tastes like you have lip-gloss on.
It looks like beetroot.

I AM

I am the day I went on my first holiday. I was three. I had my own bed beside my mum and dad, and every time you got up you would bang your head.
I am the day I went down the hill hard on my bike with my big cousin. I remember going head-over-heels and I had to get three stitches in my chin.
I am the day my aunty got a dog. It used to sit on my knee.
I am the day of my First Communion.
I am the day I first went into hospital.
I am the first time I went on stage.
I am the day of my uncle's wedding.

HAY

Hay sounds like bells ringing.
It feels like a heavy piece of thread.
It reminds me of my aunty's back garden.
I've been in a barn - cows eat this stuff.

RED

Red reminds me of Valentine's Day.

EGG

I like eggs except for the yolk.
It reminds me of my Mum making the Sunday dinner.
I would rather have it fried, along with a piece of toast.

FIRST THINGS

I saw a dark room full of dreams.
All I could think of was going to school.
I tasted Ricicles and I smelled the fresh air.

FIRE

Sometimes I put my finger through the flame, but you can't feel it a bit, because the wind makes it go in the other direction. At school we have fire-drill.

EARTH

It looks like wee bits of gravy over mashed potatoes.
It sounds like beans rolling on a plate.

WATER

Water looks like a clear glass window.
It feels like a worm on your hand.

Charlene Doherty

FIRST MEMORY

I remember my first day at school. I went into the wrong class. Then the other teacher had to come in to take me into her class. It was so shaming.

I AM

I am the day I got my first nephew.
I am the day of my sister's wedding.
I am the day I got my first niece.
I am the day of my brother's wedding.
I am the day of my First Communion.

RED

Red is the colour of an apple I have just eaten.
It sounds like a bundle of books falling.
It is all bumps and hollows.

BEST DAY

My best day was at my brother's wedding. I wore a beautiful red and white dress. I got lots of money, and I stayed for the disco with my cousins. It was brilliant.

FIRST THINGS

The first thing I saw this morning were sheep in the fields.
The first thing I heard was my nephew crying.
The first thing I felt was the quilt.
The first thing I smelt were eggs boiling on the cooker.

RESPONSE TO MUSIC

It is colourful like a rainbow.
It reminds me of a piece of music that was played at my aunty's funeral.

I HAVE A DREAM

I had a dream there was a bomb in Buncrana - that about fifteen people died, but I was thankful that none of my family was included. My neighbour was killed in the bomb. It was terrible. It was the worst dream I ever had.

HAIKU

I was coming home
From my sister's house in Meath
When I saw my dog.

FIRE

It smells like the burning of rubbish in the back yard.

183

SOIL
It feels cold.
It lives under the grass.

Eimear McAteer

I AM
I am the day that my younger brothers were born.
I am the day I split my head.
I am the night I went to hospital after I fell and burst my front lip and broke my two front teeth.
I am the day I went to Birmingham to see an Aston Villa match and they won 3:1.
I am the day of my First Communion.
I am the day we got a new car.
I am the day my new cousins were born.
I am the day I went to Jersey with my granny.

YELLOW
Yellow is the taste of bitterness.

HAY
I've seen it on my granda's farm.
It sounds like the rustling of someone opening a bag.

ORANGE
It smells like honey.
It reminds me of the orange quilt in my granny's bedroom.

MY WORST DAY
Was when my granny died. It was 4 o'clock in the morning when we got a phone-call. It was my uncle. He was ringing to say granny was very very weak and ill, so my Mum got up and packed and set off. It was a two hour drive for her. She had to travel to Leitrim. When she reached the hospital she met her sisters and brothers. When she went in she saw that my granny was very pale. That night they slept in the hospital. The next day at twelve o'clock, my granny passed away. A little while before that the nuns were praying by her bed. After they stopped praying, she closed her eyes and died. And a tear ran down her cheek. I was off school that day when we got a phone-call. That was my worst day.

I HAVE A DREAM
I have a dream that there would be peace in our country.
I have a dream that my grandad was better and out of hospital.
I have a dream I had a sister.

EGG
It looks like a jelly-fish.
It smells like a hen has just laid it.
When I hear an egg being cracked, I think of sea-shells.
It reminds me of a space-ship.

WHITE
White is the colour of the radiator in my bedroom.
White tastes like salt.
White reminds me of cold, breezy days.
When I touch white, I get the shivers.
White smells like snowdrops.

RESPONSE TO MUSIC
When I hear this song, I think of my grandad who is sick in hospital.

EARTH
It reminds me of the time when I was small and I got a biscuit and dipped
it into the earth and ate it. It was horrible.

WATER
It sounds as if someone had glue on their hand.
It looks like eye-drops for your eyes.

AIR
Air is what you take in when you get a fright.

FIRE
When I sit with my back to the fire, it feels as if I am on fire.

Shauna Bradley

FIRST MEMORY
I remember when I was five, my cousin and I were playing a game, and
she ran into the house to get a drink. I was playing on my swing, then I
ran to the door and a big gust of wind came, and the door blew closed and

185

my finger got caught in the door, and the top part fell off.

CLOVE
What they look like is flies.

I AM
I am the day of my First Communion.
I am the day when I started Irish Dancing.

STRAW
It feels like a bundle of hair.
It smells like the farm when you go to visit.
It sounds like paper being crackled up.

RED
Red smells like smelly socks.
Red feels like a metal bar.

WORST DAY
My worst day was when I got out of bed and went downstairs. When I asked my mummy what was the matter, she said *Your granda has died.*

I HAD A DREAM
I had a dream that when I got up one morning I was looking for my shoes, and I found one. I still did not find it and I looked upstairs and down. I was called for dinner. I kept looking, but had to get on my pyjamas. When I put my pyjamas on, there was my other shoe.

EGG
It feels like cod liver oil.
It reminds me of when my mummy cracked the egg and it went all over the floor.

BLUE
Blue looks like a blue eye-ball.
Blue sounds like shaking dice.

FIRST THINGS
When I woke I smelt some good cooking.
I saw my room all messed up.
I heard a lot of noise downstairs.

RESPONSE TO MUSIC

It looks like someone leaving someone else, and it reminds me when I went to my granda - to see him in the coffin.

FIRE

It sounds like fire-works.
It smells like potatoes boiling in the pot.
It reminds me of when the cooker is on.

AIR

It carries dust about.

EARTH

Earth is the safest place to live.

WATER

It sounds like you swallowing your tea.

Sarah Breslin

I REMEMBER

I remember when I was small I nearly fell in the fire, but my granda caught me.

MY PLACE

Is the way you can see Lough Swilly and some of the town from my house.

PINK

Smells like candy floss.
It feels soft and sticky.
It makes me think of a soft pillow.

I AM

I am the day I was up in my granda and granny's garden. There was a caravan site, where people come down in the week-end. Somebody scared my granda's goat and it came running around my legs with its rope on, and tripped me.
I am the day my cousins were born.
I am the day that I first came to school here.
I am the day of my First Communion.
I am the day I won a medal.

BEST DAY/WORST DAY
My best day is when I heard we were going to Lanzarote. I was so excited because I was never in a warm country before.
My worst day was when my uncle died. It was very sad to see him in the coffin.

I HAVE A DREAM
I have a dream that everyone in the world would have enough food.
I have a dream of going to America with my family.
I have a dream that I will get my room finished.

GREY
Is like dark clouds when it's going to rain.
Grey reminds me of a bad day when everything goes wrong.
It looks gloomy.
It is sharp and pointy.

CURRANT
I have seen it before, when my granny was making fruit cakes.

DREAMING
I had a dream that I lost my hair, and in the morning when I woke up, I touched my hair to see if it was there.

Ruairí McLaughlin

I REMEMBER
I remember when I was about six or seven years old, I was in a car accident. It was about 7.30 pm and I was in my car with my mum. She was driving down a long lane, going at about thirty or forty miles per hour. I was sliding to one side of the car. I slid against the handle of the door, and the door opened and I fell out. My head was split and my mum had to drive me to a doctor to get stitches.

CLOVE
It sounds like a thumb-tack dropping.

BARLEY
It tastes like Ready Brek without milk in it.
It sounds like somebody tapping easy.

I AM
I am the day I got my cat.
I am the day my aunty came home from America.

I am the time I got my Play Station.

HAY
It smells like a barn.
It sounds like somebody writing gently.

GOLD
It sounds very rich.
It looks like the sun rising.
It smells like butter.

MY BEST DAY
Was when my friend came home to stay. We had known each other for six years.

CURRANT
It tastes like a grape.
It looks like a dried bit of blood.

RESPONSE TO MUSIC
It made me feel sad.
It reminds me of my uncle.

I HAD A DREAM
That I owned my own aeroplane. One night I was flying and all the lights went out. I thought they would come back on, but they didn't. Suddenly the lights came on. I turned my head to see if they were all on, when I turned back there was a building there, then I woke up.

FIRE
Reminds me of bonfire night.
It reminds me of a wrestler.

AIR
I like taking a deep breath before running.

WATER
It reminds me of when I nearly drowned in Greece.
It feels moisty in your hands.

EARTH
Earth is the ground beneath our feet.

Andrea McNutt

MY PLACE

The place I am living in is great because it's home.
We have got lots of fields down by my house, where I can play.
My granda has a lot of trees that we can play hide and seek in.
My favourite thing is the walks my Mum takes me on. And my friends live right beside me.

RED

It makes me think of the horizon on a hot summer day.

BARLEY

It smells like a rotting carcass brought in from the plains.

I AM

I am the day we went to collect our dog from its previous owner.
I am the day that I met my only girl cousin.
I am the day I came out of hospital.
I am the day my sister was born.
I am the day I played a role in the pantomime.
I am the day I had my first Holy Communion.
I am the day I nearly drowned in the pool.
I am the day my aunty crashed.
I am the day we went to America.

HAY

It looks like grass burnt in the desert by the hot sun.
It feels crooked and bent like my dead aunt's walking stick.
It reminds me of the farm in Glenties, where my granda works.

BLACK

Black feels like a coarse hair.
Black tastes bitter and strong.
Black smells like embers of the fire where I sit on cold days drinking hot chocolate.
Black sounds like a banshee knocking and screaming at your door.   ·
Black looks like a girl's hair running in the wind.

I HAVE A DREAM

I have a dream that my granny has been cured in the hospital bed, and instead of coming home after Mass, with my mum crying at the doorstep, saying that she had just had a call from grandad saying that my granny had passed away, that it was all the other way around. That instead of going to her funeral, we were going to celebrate her getting better, and being cured. And that they had found a cure for motor neurone disease.

EGG
It tastes like an omelette just off the pan.
It looks like the sun climbing up from beneath the sea.
It feels gooey and slimy like my dog's saliva.
It reminds me of when I made a fry for my Mum in the morning.

ORANGE
It smells like a perfume my mum wears.
It sounds like a newborn baby crying.

CURRANT
It looks like the eye of my teddy lying on my bed.
It reminds me of the pudding I get every year at Christmas.

TIME
I sometimes hate time
I sometimes think time is fine
I don't dislike time.

FIRE
Its flickering in the wind reminds me of my sister full of life, as if her flame is never going to run out.
It has the bright glow of my cousin's eyes.
It reminds me of the warm summer days we spent in America.

AIR
When I am angry I hold my breath and count to ten.
When I went to the hospital I wished that the window was not open, with the wind gushing in on top of me.
When you are on top of a mountain, you wish the air wasn't so dense.
Air is the thing that makes my ears pop when I'm on a plane.

EARTH
Earth is the thing that you fall on when you trip.
Earth comes in all over our house when grandad comes in from the farm.
Earth is the thing you reach down into when you plant a tree.